A Peoples Edu

AP*/Honors

Laboratory Investigations

AP*
CHEMISTRY

DAVID HOSTAGE
MARTIN FOSSETT

Publisher: Tom Maksym

Executive Editor: Steven Jay Griffel

Editor: Richard deFuria

Vice President, Production and Manufacturing: Doreen Smith

Art Director: Eric Dawson

Production Manager: Jason Grasso

Project Manager: Steven Genzano

Production Editor: Carol Deckert

Design: Carol Deckert, Steven Genzano

Cover Design: Chris Kennedy

Illustrations: Greg Harris, Sal Esposito, Steven Genzano

Copy Editor: Dee Josephson

Proofreaders: Shelly Rawson, Donna Mattina, Josh Gillenson, Pat Smith

Permissions Manager: Kristine Liebman

This book is dedicated to the memory of Edward F. deVillafranca. "Coe" was an inspirational teacher and capable administrator for many years at The Kent School (CT). He was a legend in the Advanced Placement Chemistry community as a teacher, workshop leader, Reader, Table Leader, and member of the Test Development Committee. Hundreds of new Readers and workshop participants received Coe's gentle guidance and humorous perspective. And he was a great friend and mentor for both of us. We miss you, Coe!

* AP is a registered trademark of the College Board, which was not involved in the production of, and does not endorse, this book.

Table of Contents

Introduction

Why Study Chemistry?

You are about to embark on an exciting adventure! Chemistry—the study of matter and the changes that matter undergoes—is a fascinating discipline. This is the science that drives all others, from physics to Earth science to biology. Geologists and biologists have relied on chemistry more and more as their disciplines have shifted from a descriptive basis to an analytical one. In fact, much of modern biology has become a direct application of chemical principles. Molecular biology depends on techniques invented by Kary Mullis, a chemist from California. In the early 1980s, Dr. Mullis developed the polymerase chain reaction (PCR) technique, which revolutionized the way biologists analyze DNA. Dr. Mullis won the 1993 Nobel Prize in Chemistry for his extraordinary work.

What Will Chemistry Lab Be Like?

The laboratory is the place where chemistry comes alive. There the chemist gets to observe color changes, gas-forming reactions, and other interesting phenomena. Abstract concepts from topics such as equilibrium and kinetics are demonstrated right in front of you. Your own careful measurements and perceptive observations in the laboratory will allow you to explore and master chemistry concepts that might otherwise remain hidden between the pages of your textbook. As a student of Advanced Placement Chemistry, your work in the laboratory will give you a distinct advantage over those students with little or no lab experience.

Organization of Each Lab

The experiments in this lab manual have been designed specifically with your goals in mind—both academically and practically. First, each of the labs presents you with the opportunity to use a *variety* of common analytical procedures as you collect experimental data. Secondly, the calculations that you make as you analyze the data collected in your experiments will prepare you to answer similar free-response problems when you write the AP Chemistry Exam in May. As you will see, most of the labs have special sections devoted to chemical calculations. And third, in each lab you will practice scientific writing. The descriptions that you write as you make observations of laboratory experiments and the conclusions that you draw from them as you perform analyses will prepare you to answer free-response essay questions on the exam.

The Lab as Preparation for the AP Exam and Academic Achievement

In the back of this manual we are including a section about preparation for success in the writing of the exam. Our experience, as Readers of the AP Chemistry Examination, confirms that there is no substitute for firsthand lab experiences to help reinforce complex chemistry concepts. Remember that the roadblocks and pitfalls that are an essential part of any laboratory journey will prepare you to be a skeptical chemist, ready for the fine thinking required for the multiple-choice section of the exam. More importantly, it is during those experiences—when you are following in the footsteps of great chemists—that you absorb the wisdom and energy that will help you to rearrange ideas and direct you to express them with greater clarity.

Fun fiddling in the lab . . . the puzzles of analysis . . . direct practice for the exam . . . a boost to your chances for college admission . . . possible college credit and/or placement . . . what's not to love about the chemistry laboratory?

Laboratory Skills and Equipment

Rest assured that *all* the topics recommended for laboratory by the Test Development Committee for AP Chemistry are covered in this manual, and usually in several different ways. Yet we provide a gradual development of laboratory skills and knowledge from simple to more complex, both within individual experiments and throughout the book. And because good lab technique is essential to the chemist, the Appendices provide instruction on handling and constructing special lab apparatus. In this course you will have plenty of opportunity to fabricate and utilize—make and shake!—the apparatus.

Efficient Use of Laboratory Time and Materials

Since we have spent many, many hours in the high school chemistry lab ourselves, we have attempted to make your life as a chemistry student easier wherever possible. We know that you will not have a three- or four-hour laboratory period each week to complete complicated labs. As often as possible, we will give you a chance to accomplish as much as possible during your precious time in lab. For example, when you analyze a substance, we will try to give you several different methods of doing so. This will allow you to make comparisons of those methods. Or, your instructor may decide to select from those methods to help you to get the most from your time in the laboratory. We do not intend that you finish every possible variation of every experiment in the lab manual, and you do not need to do so to gain that "APAdvantage" before writing the exam.

We feel fortunate to have been blessed with extraordinary students during our years of teaching chemistry; in fact, many of them have tested earlier versions of these experiments. We think of those individuals who have experienced our enthusiasm for laboratory work and enjoyed it enough to continue with chemistry during their college years. Some of those students have chosen to become scientists, engineers, physicians, or educators. But ALL our students—since they breathe and metabolize—remain practicing chemists! We hope that you will have similar enriching experiences.

David Hostage
Martin Fossett

Laboratory Rules and Safety Procedures

Your instructor will have rules and policies about laboratory behavior and procedures that are unique to your situation. In addition, there are a number of safety themes that are common to *all* chemistry laboratories. These policies have been adapted from the American Chemical Society's excellent "Starting with Safety" program.

REMEMBER

Your instructor is the single most important safety feature of your laboratory. Be sure to report any mishap to her or him immediately.

1. Handling Chemicals

a. Get in the habit of looking carefully at the label every time you pick up a container. Every label should be clearly marked with chemical formula, concentration, date, and preparer.

   (*Hint:* If you place your thumb on the important part of the label before pouring a solution, you will avoid dribbling the chemical down the label.)

b. When diluting concentrated acids, add acid to distilled water and swirl continuously to dissipate the heat that is generated.

c. Do not place stoppers on the lab bench, as that may leave a trace of the chemical on the lab bench as a future surprise to someone else. Also avoid this practice because the stopper may pick up impurities from the surface of the lab bench and contaminate the chemical when it is returned to the container. Return stoppers to containers as soon as possible.

d. Surround spills with an absorbent material (such as kitty litter). Neutralize acid spills with baking soda. Neutralize base spills with vinegar.

e. Never pipet by mouth. Use a pipet bulb.

f. Volatile chemicals belong in a fume hood at all times.

2. Glassware and Burner Use

a. Always check glassware for cracks before heating it.

b. Before lighting a Bunsen (or other) burner, check the hose connection at each end. Check the hose itself for cracks or other deformities. Replace the hose if it is defective.

c. Use a striker to light the burner. If you must use matches, strike them away from you, bring the lighted match halfway up the burner, then carefully move up to the gas at the top of the burner.

3. Thermometers

a. Do not use a mercury thermometer unless absolutely necessary; breaking one leads to a mercury spill, a serious situation that must be reported immediately! Instead, use an alcohol thermometer or thermoprobe. Also, check to be sure that the range intended for the device you are using matches the temperature you are attempting to measure.

b. Remember that a thermometer itself will get hot, so be sure to allow it to cool in a protected place.

4. Glass Tubing or Rod

a. When you intentionally break glass tubing or rod, use appropriate techniques *(see Appendices)*. If you happen to break the tubing or rod by accident, clean up the shards immediately. Be sure to fire-polish the ends of a tube or rod after you have broken it.

b. Lubricate glass tubing or rod before inserting it into a rubber stopper. Glycerol works well and saliva will serve in a pinch.

5. Centrifuge Use

a. Balance the weight around the center of the centrifuge so that it will not "walk" off the table surface. If you have only one test tube, place another of the same size with a similar level of water in it directly across the center bearing of the centrifuge.

(*Hint:* You can usually find a classmate who has a tube to be centrifuged.)

b. Always allow the spinning centrifuge to slow itself down. Then apply the brake to bring the spinning to a stop. Do not try to stop a spinning centrifuge with your hand.

6. Lab Dress Code

a. Always wear a lab apron to protect your body and clothing.

b. Always wear lab goggles to protect your eyes.

c. Always wear closed-top leather shoes to protect your feet.

d. Avoid loose ends! Tie back or remove long hair, loose clothing, and dangling jewelry.

7. Lab Behavior

a. No horseplay in the lab is allowed.

b. Leave your backpack outside the lab area.

c. Do not eat or drink in the lab.

8. Safety Equipment

Be sure to know the location and use of:

a. safety telephone
b. first aid kit
c. mercury spill kit
d. eyewash station
e. safety shower
f. fire extinguisher
g. fire blanket
h. fume hood
i. electrical shut-off
j. water shut-off
k. school nurse, infirmary, or health center

Laboratory Equipment

Common Laboratory Desk Equipment

Number	Item	Number	Item
1	graduated cylinder	13	small test tube rack
2	graduated cylinder	14	glass plate
3	beakers	15	wire gauze
4	stirring rod	16	crucible tongs
5	wash bottle	17	spatula
6	funnel	18	litmus, red and blue
7	Erlenmeyer flask	19	watch glass
8	Erlenmeyer flask	20	evaporating dish
9	test tubes	21	dropping pipet
10	test tubes	22	test tube holder
11	test tubes	23	large test tube brush
12	large test tube rack	24	small test tube brush

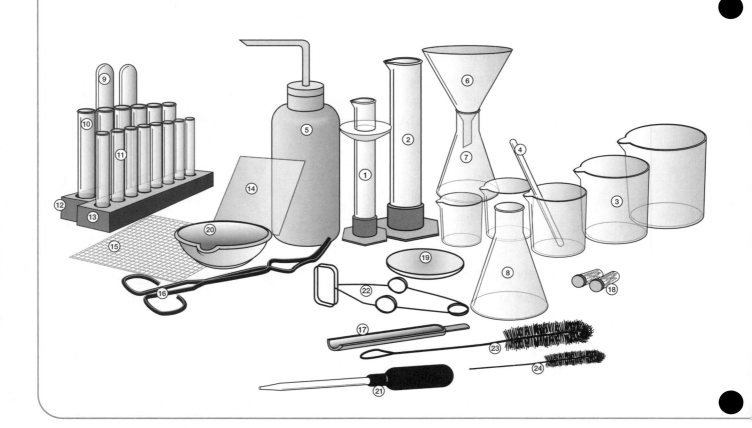

Special Laboratory Equipment

Number	Item	Number	Item
1	reagent bottle	16	porcelain crucible
2	condenser	17	mortar and pestle
3	Erlenmeyer flask	18	glass bottle
4	beaker	19	pipet
5	Petri dish	20	ring and buret stands
6	Büchner funnel	21	clamp
7	Büchner (filter) flask	22	double buret clamp
8	volumetric flasks	23	Bunsen burner
9	Florence flask	24	buret brush
10	thermometer	25	clay pipe-stem triangle
11	graduated cylinder	26	rubber stoppers
12	buret	27	wire loop for flame test
13	eudiometer	28	pneumatic trough
14	U-tube	29	rubber pipet bulb
15	porous ceramic cup	30	iron support ring

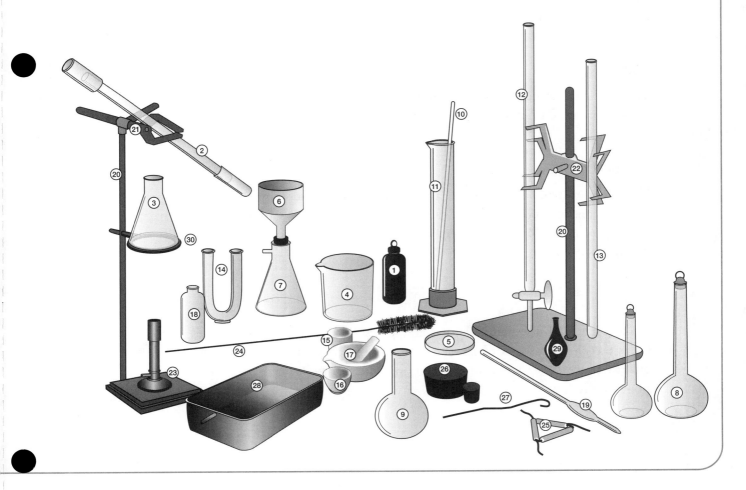

Writing the Laboratory Report

While there are many possible formats for the preparation of a laboratory report, certain key characteristics are constant. Your instructor will explain the particular requirements for his or her course. Some instructors prefer a style that resembles an article intended for publication in a scientific journal. Some are more concerned with a particular style of data presentation and analysis. Others may prefer a hand-written version on a quad-ruled page, or insist on a word-processed document. Here is one possible style that has worked well for us:

Heading with Personal Information

Include your name, date, course and class block, as well as the name of partner(s) or any other collaboration that took place.

Lab Title

Write a title that describes the nature of the lab that you performed. ("Lab 6" or "Halloween Lab" does not reveal much!)

Purpose

Write a brief statement explaining the thrust of your lab and how this goal is to be accomplished. The statement can be a simple phrase or two, but definitely should not go on for several paragraphs. What new techniques or instruments will you be learning?

Materials

Make a list of all the materials that are necessary to do the experiment, especially the chemicals used. Include the concentration of any solution. Specific quantities are not required in this section, since they will be given in the sections that follow.

Procedure

Prepare a summary of the steps that you followed while performing the experiment. Do not write detailed instructions, but do make the directions thorough enough that an intelligent person who does not specialize in chemistry could read this section and follow along.

Data and Calculations

Record all your data and results in your lab notebook neatly. Label all data, using the correct number of significant figures for any measurement that you made. Include proper units. Use tables whenever possible to summarize data. *Remember:* neatness counts!

Be sure not to confuse data (measurements that you have taken) with calculations (manipulations of your data). For each type of calculation, give a sample calculation. Show the equation you have selected and plug your data into it. If graphs are included, make each graph a suitable size and label each axis, including units.

Conclusion

A three-paragraph model works well here. First, write a brief summary of the theory behind the experiment. Define key terms and explain important theories. It is likely that you will refer to other sources when you prepare this section, so be sure to cite them correctly. Do not refer yet to this particular experiment.

In a second paragraph, discuss the results of your experiment. Error analysis is very important in AP Chemistry. Be sure to distinguish between a mistake (an avoidable mishap, such as spilling some of the solution) and an error (implicit in any measurement that you take). If you can compare your final result to some published standard, do so by calculating a percent error, then explain why the error is as small or as large as it is. If you are close to the standard value, it may be as a result of *offsetting errors*, rather than a sterling example of your perfection in the laboratory. Which measurement contributed most to the error of your result? Which contributed least?

In the final paragraph, write a concluding statement. Did you meet the purpose of the experiment? If you were to perform the experiment again with exactly the same procedure, how could you make the lab work better? Could you suggest modifications to the technique to make the experiment work better? Be an inventive scientist here! This is perhaps the most important statement that you can make in the report, because you must understand fully what you have done in the experiment, and why, in order to think critically about how to improve it.

Also: be sure to answer any questions presented in the text of the experiment in this lab manual. Give the number of each question and answer it directly.

Finally, remember that the quality of your lab reports is important for far more than the grade that you receive for each one! Your lab notebook, a compendium of all the effort that you have exerted in lab and in writing each report, will serve as a valuable resource as you review for the AP Chemistry examination in May. If you have written good reports, it will be easier for you to review important passages of theory and samples of key calculations. Additionally, the chemistry departments at some colleges and universities will ask to see your lab notebook so that they can ascertain that you have completed a lab program comparable to their in-house version. We predict that your good report of your completion of the labs in this lab manual will find favor with your college or university.

Name _____   Date _____

Instructor _____   Section _____

Experiment

1

An Introduction to Qualitative Analysis

PURPOSE

- Research and organize data on solubility, color change, gas reactions, and other physical characteristics used in qualitative analysis
- Determine the presence or absence of ions in unknown solutions

---

INTRODUCTION

Qualitative analysis, or **QA,** is a system to determine the presence or absence of certain cations or anions in solution. By mixing certain reagents in a certain order under certain conditions, precipitates are formed that confirm the presence of certain ions. Qualitative analysis is also known as **selective precipitation.**

There are many QA schemes. One abbreviated version is illustrated below, but because it includes steps to precipitate certain cations with sulfides, it can be problematic due to difficulties with the source of the sulfide ion. Historically a hydrogen sulfide gas generator was employed, but the toxicity of that gas has deterred the use of this technique. The organic molecule thioacetamide can also be used as a sulfide source, but poor storage longevity and suspected carcinogenicity have deterred this strategy, too. Other sulfide sources have been suggested, as have other schemes that avoid the use of the sulfide ion entirely.

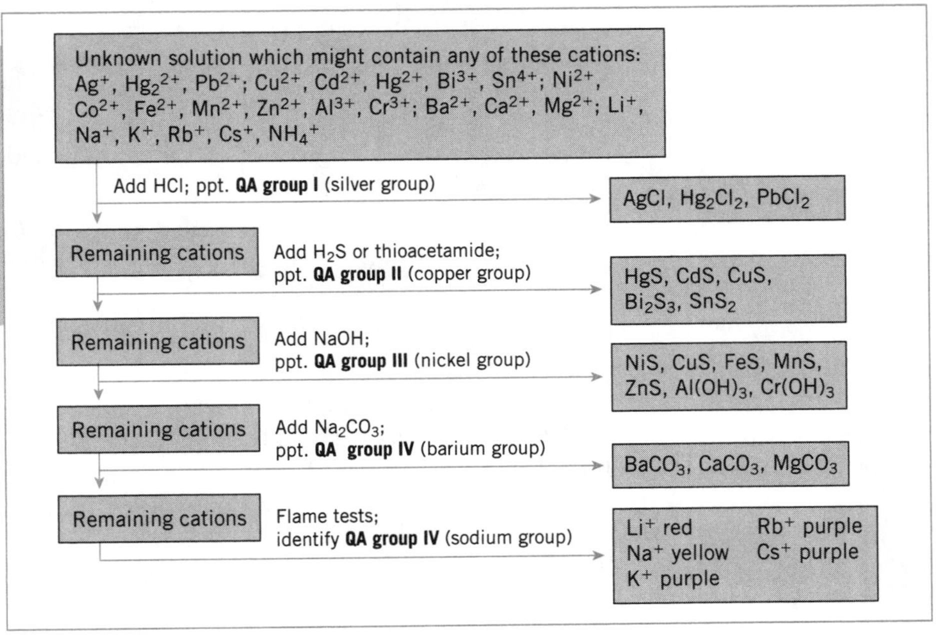

Figure 1.1

A flow diagram for a traditional QA scheme that uses sulfide to selectively precipitate certain cations.

Unknown solution which might contain any of these cations:
Ag^+, Hg_2^{2+}, Pb^{2+}; Cu^{2+}, Cd^{2+}, Hg^{2+}, Bi^{3+}, Sn^{4+}; Ni^{2+}, Co^{2+}, Fe^{2+}, Mn^{2+}, Zn^{2+}, Al^{3+}, Cr^{3+}; Ba^{2+}, Ca^{2+}, Mg^{2+}; Li^+, Na^+, K^+, Rb^+, Cs^+, NH_4^+

Add HCl; ppt. **QA group I** (silver group) → $AgCl$, Hg_2Cl_2, $PbCl_2$

Remaining cations — Add H_2S or thioacetamide; ppt. **QA group II** (copper group) → HgS, CdS, CuS, Bi_2S_3, SnS_2

Remaining cations — Add NaOH; ppt. **QA group III** (nickel group) → NiS, CuS, FeS, MnS, ZnS, $Al(OH)_3$, $Cr(OH)_3$

Remaining cations — Add Na_2CO_3; ppt. **QA group IV** (barium group) → $BaCO_3$, $CaCO_3$, $MgCO_3$

Remaining cations — Flame tests; identify **QA group IV** (sodium group) → Li^+ red Rb^+ purple Na^+ yellow Cs^+ purple K^+ purple

Although such elaborate schemes are useful in determining the presence of unknown cations in solution, much can also be learned by the thoughtful comparison of a set of solutions with a list of their identities. Luckily, this process is not nearly so complicated.

There are certain indications that are evidence that a chemical reaction has occurred. Among these are

➤ evolution of energy (heat, light, or other electromagnetic radiation);

➤ change in color of a solution;

➤ change of phase (formation of a new solid, liquid, or gas);

➤ rupture and/or formation of covalent bonds (*Note:* in many reactions this process is neither readily observed nor apparent).

Procedure Preview There is a certain body of information to master before starting a qualitative analysis investigation. First and foremost, the ability to predict precipitation reactions is needed. Second, knowledge of the color of certain ions in solution is useful. Third, as certain common reactions release a new gas, presence of gases is often good evidence. Be sure to familiarize yourself with these groups of characteristics, given in abbreviated form below, before proceeding with your experiment.

Precipitation Reactions and KISS Guidelines

The KISS (**K**eep **I**t **S**imple **S**olubility) Guidelines make a complicated topic approachable. This simplified five-step set of solubility guidelines is very serviceable, allowing accurate prediction of precipitation in many instances. If you need a more precise idea of the actual solubility of a salt, you must consult with a table of K_{sp}, or **solubility product constant**, values.

Remember:

All salts containing (insert any ion from Guidelines 1–4) are *soluble*.

The Cation Guideline:

1. Na^+, NH_4^+, K^+

The Anion Guidelines:

2. NO_3^-, $C_2H_3O_2^-$, ClO_3^-/ClO_4^-

3. Halides ($Cl^-/Br^-/I^-$) *except* when paired with the Silver Group cations: Ag^+, Hg_2^{2+}, Pb^{2+}

4. SO_4^{2-} *except* when paired with the Silver Group and Ba^{2+} and Sr^{2+}

The "Catch-all" Guideline:

5. Everything else is assumed to be *insoluble*.

Thus, the salt NaCl is assumed to be soluble (see guidelines 1 and 3); $Al(NO_3)_3$ is soluble (see guideline 2); and $NH_4C_2H_3O_2$ is soluble (see guidelines 1 and 2). But $BaSO_4$ is not soluble (see guideline 4) and combining the barium and sulfate ions in solution will result in a precipitate.

Troubleshooting Guideline 5 is especially useful. Memorize the few salts that *are* soluble, rather than the many that are not!

Colors of Certain Ions in Solution

Cation	Color
Cu^{2+}	blue
Ni^{2+}	green
Co^{2+}	blue
Fe^{3+}	pale yellow

Anion	Color
CrO_4^{2-}	yellow
$Cr_2O_7^{2-}$	orange
MnO_4^-	violet

Gas-producing Reactions

Certain combinations of solutions will produce gases that can be seen as bubbles or perceived as distinctive aromas. One way to remember these combinations is to know that they produce certain "phantoms," or compounds whose formula you might predict as a product. These phantom products, which are unstable, break down immediately into water and a gas and must not be left in a net ionic equation. They include carbonic acid ("H_2CO_3"), sulfurous acid ("H_2SO_3"), and ammonium hydroxide ("NH_4OH").

Figure 1.2
The release of gases in certain common reactions can provide important evidence in performing qualitative analysis.

Here are some useful reactions to remember:

➤ An acid will react with a carbonate to produce carbon dioxide gas (bubbles):

$$2\,H^+_{(aq)} + CO_3^{2-}_{(aq)} \rightarrow \text{“}H_2CO_3\text{”}_{(aq)} \rightarrow H_2O_{(l)} + CO_{2(g)}$$

➤ An acid will react with sulfite ion to produce sulfur dioxide (distinctive aroma):

$$2\,H^+_{(aq)} + SO_3^{2-}_{(aq)} \rightarrow \text{“}H_2SO_3\text{”}_{(aq)} \rightarrow H_2O_{(l)} + SO_{2(g)}$$

➤ A base will react with ammonium cation to produce ammonia (distinctive aroma):

$$NH_4^+_{(aq)} + OH^-_{(aq)} \rightarrow \text{“}NH_4OH\text{”}_{(aq)} \rightarrow H_2O_{(l)} + NH_{3(g)}$$

➤ An acid will react with sulfide ions to produce hydrogen sulfide (distinctive aroma):

$$2\,H^+_{(aq)} + S^{2-}_{(aq)} \rightarrow H_2S_{(g)}$$

These hints are well worth remembering!

A multisolution mystery should be solved in two separate steps. The first requires some research. It will involve your knowledge of solubilities, colors of ions in solution, and gas-producing reactions. Some additional work in common chemistry resources (your chemistry textbook, the *CRC Handbook of Chemistry and Physics*, *Lange's Handbook of Chemistry*, the *Merck Index*, certain Internet sites, and so on) will help you to predict colors of precipitates, among other information.

First, create a "Table of Knowns" as a table in a word processing document or spreadsheet (see **Table 1.1** as an example). List the known formulas both across the top and down the left side of the table. In each cell of the table, you should note what (if anything) you expect to see if a solution of the compounds corresponding to that cell is mixed. Note any possible sign of a chemical reaction: precipitation *(ppt)* of an insoluble salt, gas formation, color changes in solution, evolution of heat, or anything else. When using the handbooks, be sure to look up the solubilities and colors of hydrated salts (of the form • $x\mathrm{H_2O}$), not the anhydrates, since the precipitates in this experiment are forming in aqueous solutions. If no reaction is predicted, write NAR for "no apparent reaction."

MATERIALS

➤ texts/chemistry resource handbooks
➤ series of unknown ionic solutions (*to be provided by instructor*)
➤ disposable pipets
➤ microwell plate

PROCEDURE

Step A Once you have finished your research, you may come into the lab. Prepare a "Table of Unknowns," similar to the "Table of Knowns," but at this point without any labels on the rows and columns. In the lab you will find a series of bottles marked with identifying symbols (letters, numbers, etc.), each containing one of the solutions from the Table of Knowns. You will not be told which is which—figuring that out is the goal of the experiment. Label the columns and rows of the "Table of Unknowns" with these symbols.

Step B Label a series of disposable pipets with the symbols from the bottles, then draw a bulbful of each solution from the appropriate stock bottle. Take a microwell plate to serve as a stand for the pipets *and* to allow you to mix the solutions in all possible pairs. Watch carefully for any sign of reaction and note this into the "Table of Unknowns."

Step C Once both tables have been filled in, a few minutes of careful comparison will enable you to identify each of the unknown solutions. If you are clever, you will realize that it is not necessary to mix every possible pair. Remember: the *absence* of any chemical change when two solutions are mixed is also valuable information.

Example

Suppose that you are given a list of five solutions to sort out, including solutions of these salts:

- copper(II) sulfate
- potassium chloride
- potassium permanganate
- potassium sulfide
- silver nitrate

Several of the solutions can be identified quickly without performing any mixes. The copper(II) sulfate and potassium permanganate solutions have characteristic colors, while the potassium sulfide solution has an unforgettable aroma. The other two are both colorless and odorless but they can be separated quickly by performing a mix or two.

Table 1.1

A possible "Table of Knowns," predicting reactions and identifying colors of precipitates, evolution of gas, or other changes.

	$CuSO_4$	KCl	$KMnO_4$	K_2S	$AgNO_3$
$CuSO_4$	XXXX*	NAR	$Cu(MnO_4)_2$	CuS Black ppt	Ag_2SO_4 White ppt
KCl	XX*	XXXX	NAR	NAR	AgCl White ppt
$KMnO_4$	XX	XX	XXXX	NAR	$AgMnO_4$ Violet ppt
K_2S	XX	XX	XX	XXXX	Ag_2S Black ppt
$AgNO_3$	XX	XX	XX	XX	XXXX

*It is unnecessary to fill in more than half the Table. There is no point in noting that a solution does not react with itself (the diagonal XXXX cells), nor is there any reason to repeat a mix already performed in a different order (the XX cells).

You already have three solutions identified by color or aroma. To separate the silver nitrate and potassium chloride solutions, you might mix them independently with the potassium sulfide solution. The mixture silver nitrate + potassium sulfide will yield a black precipitate, whereas the potassium chloride + potassium sulfide mixture will give no apparent reaction. There are other ways to pursue this identification. Look carefully at the table to convince yourself of this.

**Post-Lab
Questions**

1. Complete the Table of Knowns by conferring with chemistry handbooks and other sources.

_____

_____

_____

_____

_____

_____

_____

_____

_____

_____

2. Complete the Table of Unknowns by making observations of color,
aroma, and other physical characteristics. Then make the minimum
number of solution mixes possible to allow you to conclusively identify
the other solutions.

_____

_____

_____

_____

_____

_____

_____

_____

_____

_____

_____

3. Write a **net ionic equation** (NIE) for any reaction that you predicted
in the Table of Knowns.

_____

_____

_____

_____

_____

_____

Experiment

2

Synthesis of an Alum

PURPOSE

- Synthesize a crystal of an alum
- Calculate the theoretical and percent yields of the synthesis of the alum

INTRODUCTION

According to the McGraw-Hill *Dictionary of Chemical Terms*, an **alum** is "any of a group of double sulfates of trivalent metals . . . and a univalent metal." The alum is always accompanied by twelve water molecules to form a dodecahydrate, with six waters surrounding the trivalent cation and six around the univalent cation. The most common alum is potassium aluminum(III) sulfate dodecahydrate, $KAl(SO_4)_2 \cdot 12H_2O$. It is consumed in great quantities by the paper industry, where it is used to help fillers bind to the wood fibers that make up paper, making the product less porous and less absorbent.

Many other alums are known. The univalent cation can be Li^+, Na^+, K^+, NH_4^+, or even Ag^+, and the trivalent cation can be Al^{3+}, Fe^{3+}, Cr^{3+}, or Mn^{3+}. Although the anion of an alum is usually sulfate, alums containing SeO_4^{2-} are also known. There is a unifying physical characteristic of all these alums. They form isomorphic crystals, meaning all similar in crystal pattern and in crystal size. It can be gratifying to form these crystals by slowly cooling a hot aqueous solution containing a univalent and a trivalent cation, along with sulfate anions. The solution becomes temporarily supersaturated, and this unstable situation resolves by crystallizing solid until the solution is just saturated at room temperature. The resulting solid can be a spectacularly large and well-shaped crystal.

Procedure Preview This experiment will introduce you to several fascinating aspects of the chemistry of aluminum and its compounds. Aluminum metal reacts with either strong acids or strong bases. Aluminum(III) hydroxide, one step in this reaction process, is called **amphiprotic** (or alternatively **amphoteric**) because it dissolves in either acid or in base. Here is a verbal flowchart to help you keep track of the progress of the reaction:

1. Aluminum metal, Al, is dissolved in excess strong base, OH^-, to form:
2. Tetrahydroxoaluminate(III) complex ion, $Al(OH)_4^-$, known as "aluminate," which reacts in strong acid to form:
3. Solid aluminum(III) hydroxide, $Al(OH)_3$, which dissolves in excess strong acid to form:

4. Hexaquoaluminum(III) complex ion, $Al(H_2O)_6^{3+}$, which combines with available potassium cations and sulfate anions to crystallize as:

5. Solid potassium aluminum(III) sulfate dodecahydrate, $KAl(SO_4)_2 \cdot 12H_2O$, known as "potassium alum."

MATERIALS

➤ aluminum (foil, scrap, or reagent)   ➤ 250-mL beaker
➤ 3 *M* KOH   ➤ 100-mL beaker
➤ 9 *M* H_2SO_4 ➤ hot plate or Bunsen burner
➤ ethanol solution   ➤ fume hood
➤ filter paper and filter funnel   ➤ Büchner funnel

PROCEDURE

Step A Measure out approximately 2.000 g of aluminum. Although it is not important to have exactly this amount, it *is* important to know precisely how much you start with. If using aluminum foil, rip it into as many small scraps as possible. If using aluminum scrap, cut it into as many small pieces as possible.

Step B Because hydrogen gas and a great deal of heat will be generated, the following step must be performed in a fume hood. Dissolve the aluminum by adding it slowly to 30.0 mL of 3 *M* KOH in a 250-mL (or larger) beaker. Mix thoroughly with a glass stirring rod and be careful not to allow hot solution to splatter out of the beaker. Preweigh a piece of filter paper. After the reaction is complete, use the filter paper in a funnel to filter the hot solution by gravity to remove any remaining particles. Remove the filter paper from the funnel, set it onto a watch glass, and allow it to dry overnight in the drying oven. Mass the filter paper and its particulates.

Step C Transfer the now-filtered solution to a 100-mL beaker. To this solution, add 25.0 mL 9 *M* H_2SO_4, *slowly*, with constant stirring. You will see the formation of a bright white precipitate that will then redissolve as you add more acid.

Step D Heat the solution at a low setting until the solution is completely clear. Move the beaker to a place where it will not be disturbed and cover it with a watch glass or filter paper. Allow crystallization to occur overnight.

Step E Using a Büchner funnel, suction filtration to capture the crystal(s) that have formed. Wash the crystal(s) with two 25-mL portions of ethanol solution to dry the crystals.

Step F Measure the room temperature.

Step G Measure the mass of the crystals.

Figure 2.1 After allowing crystallization to occur, collect the alum crystals by filtering under suction through a Büchner funnel.

PROCEDURE
(continued)

Calculations

1. Using your original mass of aluminum, calculate the theoretical yield of alum. Then use your data to calculate percent yield of your lab work.
2. Subtract the mass of nonreacting solid particles from Step B of the procedure from the original mass of aluminum and recalculate theoretical and percent yields.
3. Not all of the alum crystallizes from solution. To account for the dissolved alum, look up the solubility of alum in water in the CRC or other reference book. If the value is not given for the particular temperature at which you ran your lab (refer to Step F), estimate a value using the published values. Use this information to calculate the mass of alum that must have remained in solution and add it to the mass of alum crystals. Recalculate the theoretical and percent yields of alum.

Post-Lab Questions

1. What is an alum? Name at least one alum that does not contain any aluminum. How are alums used?

   _____

   _____

   _____

2. What is a **single replacement reaction**? Write a balanced equation to describe the reaction in this experiment that falls into this category of reaction.

   _____

   _____

   _____

3. What is a **synthesis reaction**? Write a balanced equation to describe the reaction in this experiment that falls into this category.

   _____

   _____

   _____

4. What is a **double replacement reaction**? Write a balanced equation to describe the reaction in this experiment that falls into this category.

   _____

   _____

   _____

5. How can you be sure that aluminum is the limiting reactant in this experiment? Show equations and calculations to support this idea.

   _____

   _____

   _____

6. What is a **complex ion**? Write a balanced equation to describe the reaction in this experiment that forms an ion in this category.

   _____

   _____

   _____

7. What is an **alloy**? What are the general types of alloys and which type is found in this experiment?

   _____

   _____

   _____

   _____

8. What is an **amphoteric** substance? How does it differ from an **amphiprotic** substance? How do these terms apply to this experiment?

   _____

   _____

   _____

9. Describe the process called **crystallization**. Be sure to include the terms **unsaturated, saturated,** and **supersaturated** solution in your explanation.

   _____

   _____

   _____

   _____

10. In this experiment, you used two different types of filtration processes. What were they, and why did you use each one?

    _____

    _____

    _____

11. What is an **MSDS**? Include in your report an MSDS for one of the chemicals that you have used in this experiment.

    _____

    _____

    _____

    _____

Name _____   Date _____

Instructor _____   Section _____

Experiment

3   Analysis of an Alum

PURPOSE

- Analyze a number of characteristics of an alum crystal
- Determine the percentage of water in a hydrate
- Compare several analytical techniques for effectiveness

INTRODUCTION

An important feature of the chemistry laboratory is **analysis**, which allows the characterization and identification of chemical compounds. These procedures include both **qualitative analysis**, a series of techniques that allow you to determine the presence or absence of a particular ion, and **quantitative analysis**, which permits you to determine how much of a certain ion or substance is there.

Qualitative analysis can be as simple as direct observation of the shape, size, and color of a crystal. Alternatively, you might use a flame test to look for the characteristic color emitted by an excited cation. Qualitative analysis could also involve a more complicated laboratory program that exploits the solubility characteristics of different compounds. In general, this approach would mean that cations are separated into five groups based on their solubility properties. The ions within each group are then separated by selectively dissolving and precipitating compounds of those ions. Finally, specific tests are used to confirm the presence of certain ions.

Quantitative analysis can include tests of varying complexities. You can look for certain physical characteristics of a substance, such as density, melting point, or boiling point. Or you can use **gravimetric analysis**, a technique by which one precipitates a certain ion and masses the results. Another method is the analysis of the amount of water in a compound by massing it, then heating it to drive off all water and massing again.

Procedure Preview A thorough investigation of a substance should include both qualitative and quantitative techniques. In this laboratory investigation, you will gain valuable experience in employing each of these techniques, as appropriate.

MATERIALS

➤ 0.5 M HCl

➤ 0.100 M $Sr(NO_3)_2$ solution

➤ alum crystal (synthesized from Experiment 2 or purchased)

➤ 15 M NH_3

➤ 3 M NH_3

➤ 6 M NaOH

➤ aluminon reagent

➤ 6 M HCl

➤ mortar and pestle

➤ flame loop

➤ capillary tubes

➤ melting point apparatus

➤ crucible

➤ centrifuge

➤ centrifuge tubes

➤ litmus paper

PROCEDURE

I. Flame test analysis for K^+ cation

Step A Using a mortar and pestle, crush a small sample of your crystal.

Step B Heat a flame loop to red-hot in a Bunsen burner flame and then carefully plunge the loop into 0.5 M HCl. Repeat. Heat the loop to red-hot one final time.

Step C Pick up a small sample of the crushed alum on the hot loop and move it slowly from the outer edge to the hottest part of the Bunsen burner flame.

Step D Observe the resulting color of the flame test.

II. Analysis for melting point

Step A Using a small sample of alum that you crushed in the previous procedure, prepare at least three capillary tubes for melting point analysis. Tap the open end of the capillary tube into the crushed alum. Invert the capillary tube and drop it down a length of glass tubing that is held upright from a hard surface. Bouncing the capillary tube in this fashion several times will compact the sample of alum at the closed end of the capillary tube. Repeat this process until about 0.5 cm of alum crystals are packed in the capillary tube.

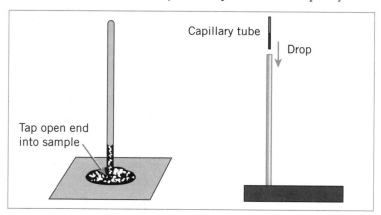

Capillary tube

Drop

Tap open end into sample

Figure 3.1

Step B Insert the capillary tubes into the Mel-Temp II melting point device and set the rheostat to allow a slow but steady increase in the temperature of the device. Your instructor may instruct you to use a different melting point apparatus or even a microscale approach.

Step C Observe the temperature when the edges of the sample of crushed alum begin to look "wet." Average the three temperatures that you observed and compare that temperature to the melting point listed for this alum in the *CRC* or other chemical reference book.

PROCEDURE
(continued)

III. Qualitative analysis for Al^{3+} cation

Step A Dissolve a small quantity of your sample of alum in distilled water.

Step B Place approximately 0.5 mL (10 or 12 drops) of your solution into a small test tube. Carefully add one drop at a time of 15 M NH_3 to make the solution basic (you can check with litmus paper, which turns blue in base). Be sure to mix well after each drop.

Step C Add two or three drops of 15 M NH_3 in excess.
  Qualitative evidence: a white, gelatinous precipitate of $Al(OH)_3$ should form.

Step D Carefully add several drops more of 15 M NH_3. $Al(OH)_3$ will not dissolve in excess 15 M NH_3.

Step E Centrifuge the test tube. Pour off the solution above the solid into an approved waste container. To the solid, add several drops of 6 M NaOH.
  Qualitative evidence: $Al(OH)_3$ is soluble in excess NaOH.

Step F Acidify the solution by adding several drops of 6 M HCl. Mix well after each drop and check with litmus paper, which turns red in acid.

Step G Add several drops of aluminon reagent (aurin tricarboxylic acid) and mix well. Then add drops of 3 M NH_3 until the solution is just basic (check with litmus paper). Place the test tube into a hot water bath for several minutes.
  Qualitative evidence: formation of a scarlet-red color confirms the presence of the Al^{3+} cation.

IV. Gravimetric analysis* for SO_4^{2-} anion

Step A Mass approximately 1 g of your crystal.

Step B Dissolve the crystal in approximately 50 mL distilled water.

Step C Add _____ mL of 0.100 M $Sr(NO_3)_2$ solution. Use stoichiometry to calculate the exact volume of $Sr(NO_3)_2$ required, then double it.

Step D Heat the precipitate and solution to near boiling and keep it at that temperature for fifteen minutes to digest the solid. In this process, the smallest particles of the precipitate will redissolve, then accrete onto the largest remaining particles. Larger particles can be more effectively filtered out of the solution.

Step E Use gravity filtration to collect as much as possible of the precipitate.

Step F Dry the filter paper and precipitate in the drying oven overnight.

Step G Mass the filter paper and precipitate.

V. Analysis for Percentage of Water in a Hydrate

Step A Mass approximately 1 g of your crystal.

Step B Transfer the crystal to a dry crucible of which you already have the mass.

Step C Heat the crucible gently, with its lid on, for five minutes.

Step D Move the lid akimbo and reheat gently for another five minutes.

Step E Allow to cool, then mass.

Step F Reheat the crucible with its lid on for five minutes more.

Step G Allow to cool, then mass. If the mass has not changed significantly, then you are done. If the mass has changed significantly, repeat the heating and massing process until it does not change significantly.

*Alternate direction for this analytic test: Repeat procedure IV for precipitation of $AlPO_4$, but substitute Na_3PO_4 solution for $Sr(NO_3)_2$ solution in order to precipitate $AlPO_4$.

PROCEDURE
(continued)

VI. Analysis of crystal

Step A Examine the color of a freshly prepared crystal of your product.

Step B Compare the color to that listed in the *CRC* or other chemistry reference book.

Step C Examine the shape of a freshly prepared crystal of your product and sketch it in your notebook. Use a magnifying glass if necessary.

Step D Compare the shape to that listed in the *CRC* or other chemistry reference book. Use a set of models or textbook diagrams to aid you.

Post-Lab Questions

1. Use the data you have collected to calculate the mass percentage of each ion and water in your alum.

2. Using the published formula of alum, calculate the theoretical mass percentages of each ion and water in the crystal.

3. Are there any differences between the two sets of percentages? Explain. Consistent with your data, discuss one potential source of error in detail.

   _____

   _____

   _____

   _____

   _____

4. Which of the analysis techniques used was most effective? Why? Which was least effective? Why?

   _____

   _____

   _____

   _____

   _____

Name _____   Date _____

Instructor _____   Section _____

4

Hess's Law: Determining the Enthalpy Change of a Reaction

PURPOSE

- Collect experimental data from which to calculate ΔH for certain reactions
- Use Hess's Law to calculate ΔH_f indirectly for MgO
- Determine and explain percent error for the calculation

INTRODUCTION

An important branch of chemistry is **thermodynamics**, the study of energy and its transformations. One way of stating the **First Law of Thermodynamics** is to remember that energy in the universe is a finite quantity; as such, it can neither be created nor destroyed. An object can contain energy in two forms—as kinetic energy (the energy of motion) or as potential energy (energy stored as a position and poised to be expressed as movement). Energy can be transferred in two different forms: work (w) and heat (q).

$$\Delta E = q + w$$

Work is defined as a force expressed over a distance, but in most chemical solutions there is no work performed, since ions in solution do not exert any force over a distance. Given that the First Law tells us that energy is finite, we can track the energy change in a chemical reaction by measuring the heat transferred from one situation to another.

In chemistry, such heat is frequently measured under constant pressure conditions and is called **enthalpy** (**H**). ΔH, the change in enthalpy, is given in molar quantities. This change is a comparison of the enthalpies of the products after the reaction to the enthalpies of the reactants before the reaction. Thus,

$$\Delta H = H_{\text{final situation}} - H_{\text{initial situation}} = H_{\text{products}} - H_{\text{reactants}}$$

A negative value for ΔH indicates that heat energy has been released by the reaction to its surroundings, therefore called an **exothermic** reaction and causing a rise in the temperature of the surroundings. An **endothermic** reaction draws heat from its surroundings (causing a temperature drop) and is assigned a positive ΔH.

The measurement of enthalpy as heat flows from one place to another is called **calorimetry**; a device used to measure such heat flow is called a **calorimeter**. Because heat is frequently measured in nonmolar quantities, q will be used and then converted later to molar quantities H. The heat released by an exothermic reaction can be absorbed both by the solution within which the reaction occurs and by the calorimeter itself. Thus,

$$q_{\text{lost by reaction}} = q_{\text{gained by solution}} + q_{\text{gained by calorimeter}}$$

$$= m\, c\, \Delta T + C_{\text{calorimeter}} \Delta T$$

where m indicates the mass of the solution, c is the specific heat capacity of the solution, ΔT is the change in temperature as the reaction progresses, and $C_{\text{calorimeter}}$ represents the heat capacity of the calorimeter.

Procedure Preview To complete this experiment, you will apply **Hess's Law** to a series of three reactions in order to calculate the **heat of formation** (ΔH_f) for a reaction that you cannot measure directly:

$$Mg_{(s)} + \frac{1}{2} O_{2(g)} \rightarrow MgO_{(s)} \qquad\qquad \Delta H_f = \underline{\ ?\ }\ \text{kJ/mol}$$

You will need to make mass, volume, and temperature measurements, then convert them into enthalpy data, using these equations:

$$Q = mc\,\Delta T \qquad\qquad Q = C_{\text{cal}} \Delta T \qquad\qquad \Delta H = -Q/\text{mol}$$

Following the steps in the procedure given below, you will collect data from which you can calculate ΔH for these reactions:

$$Mg_{(s)} + 2\,H^+_{(aq)} \rightarrow H_{2(g)} + Mg^{2+}_{(aq)} \qquad\qquad \Delta H = \underline{\ ?\ }\ \text{kJ/mol}$$

$$MgO_{(s)} + 2\,H^+_{(aq)} \rightarrow H_2O_{(l)} + Mg^{2+}_{(aq)} \qquad \Delta H = \underline{\ ?\ }\ \text{kJ/mol}$$

You will also need to look up the heat of formation of liquid water:

$$H_{2(g)} + \frac{1}{2} O_{2(g)} \rightarrow H_2O_{(l)} \qquad\qquad \Delta H_f = \underline{\ ?\ }\ \text{kJ/mol}$$

Also note: The density of $3M$ HCl is 1.050 g/mL and its specific heat capacity is somewhat less than that of pure water (4.05 J/g °C).

Troubleshooting A calorimeter will be used to ensure that all reactions are approximately **adiabatic,** that is, run under conditions in which there must be no appreciable heat exchange between the reaction system of the calorimeter and its surroundings. A "coffee cup calorimeter" works well, but *exercise caution:* a thermometer is quite heavy compared to plastic cups. It is possible to tip over your calorimeter, breaking the thermometer, spilling acid, and ruining your experiment. Be sure to place any laboratory assembly into a solid base to prevent such accidents.

Figure 4.1

A "coffee cup" calorimeter can be easily assembled using stacked polystyrene cups.

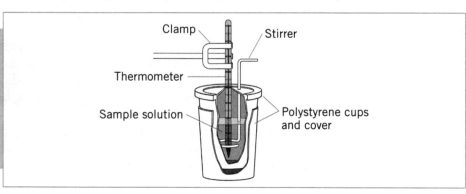

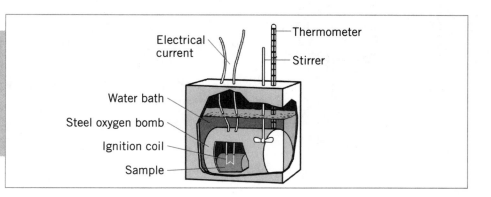

Figure 4.2
A bomb calorimeter, if available, will provide very precise heat readings.

Thermometer
Electrical current
Stirrer
Water bath
Steel oxygen bomb
Ignition coil
Sample

MATERIALS

➤ calorimeter *(see illustrations)*
➤ 3 *M* HCl
➤ magnesium ribbon
➤ MgO powder
➤ hot water bath (maintain a rolling boil for best results)
➤ glass volumetric flask (or graduated cylinder)
➤ beaker tongs (or clamp)

PROCEDURE

Step A Determine the **heat capacity** (C_{cal}) of the calorimeter by adding to it 50.00 mL of room temperature water (note the exact temperature). Measure 50.00 mL of water into a glass volumetric flask or glass graduated cylinder. Place the entire system (water in measuring device) into a hot water bath to allow the system to attain the temperature of the hot water bath. Using beaker tongs or test tube clamp, remove the now-hot volumetric flask or graduated cylinder from the hot water bath and add the 50.00 mL of hot water (you must note the exact temperature first) to the cold water. Swirl continuously until the temperature reaches equilibrium. Note the temperature to the closest 0.01°C.

Step B Add 100.00 mL 3 *M* HCl to a calorimeter cup. Cover the cup and insert a temperature-measuring device. Be sure that the temperature is constant before proceeding.

Step C Obtain a length of magnesium ribbon 100 to 150 mm long and mass it. Fold the ribbon loosely into a shape that will fit into the bottom of the calorimeter. Then drop the ribbon into the acid in the calorimeter. Swirl the calorimeter continuously, noting the highest temperature reached.

Step D Dispose of the acid and magnesium cation solution. Rinse the calorimeter with room temperature water.

Step E Repeat Steps B and C, but substitute approximately 0.500 g MgO for the Mg ribbon. Be sure that all the MgO powder goes into the acid and does not stick to the sides of the calorimeter.

Answer the following questions to prepare for making your lab report.

1. Show all data measured in appropriate, labeled tables. Be sure not to confuse data and calculations.

2. Calculate C_{cal} of the calorimeter assembly.

3. Calculate the mass of 100.00 mL of 3 M HCl.

4. Calculate Q for each reaction.

5. Calculate the number of moles of Mg and of MgO that you used.

6. Calculate ΔH for each reaction in kJ/mol.

7. Use Hess's Law to calculate ΔH_f for MgO. Show clearly how you added the reactions and enthalpy values.

8. Look up a value for ΔH_f for MgO in your textbook or in a handbook. Compare this to your value and calculate the percent error.

9. Report possible causes of error in the experiment. Indicate how each error would affect your final reported value and how significant the error might be.

_____

_____

_____

_____

_____

_____

_____

_____

10. In the theory review section of your report, be sure to include a discussion of enthalpy, calorimetry, and Hess's Law to showcase your understanding of these topics.

Name _____   Date _____

Instructor _____   Section _____

Experiment

5

Determining Mass Percent of $Mg(OH)_2$ in an Antacid Tablet

PURPOSE
- Determine the mass percent of $Mg(OH)_2$ in an antacid tablet, using both titration and gravimetric analysis
- Compare the solubilities of several salts, including $Mg(OH)_2$

INTRODUCTION

As one of the common measures of concentration used to describe a solution, the mass ratio is valuable. This is a simple comparison of the mass of a solute (the minor component of a solution) to the mass of the total solution (comprised of the solute plus the solvent, the major component of the solution). To convert this ratio to **mass percent**, multiply by 100 to move the decimal point two places and change the label to %:

$$\left(\frac{\text{g solute}}{\text{g solute + g solvent}}\right) \times 100 = \text{mass \%}$$

In the lab, one can usually find the overall mass of a solution easily, by direct physical measurement with a scale. Finding the mass of one component can be more challenging.

Procedure Preview In this lab you will have the opportunity to determine the mass of a single component (magnesium hydroxide) of a larger mixture (an antacid tablet) in two different ways. One technique will employ an acid-base titration to determine the number of hydroxide ions present. The other will precipitate all magnesium cations present in the form of an insoluble salt, which can then be dried and massed. In either case, application of stoichiometry will allow you to calculate the amount of magnesium hydroxide present. This value can then be compared to the total mass of the tablet to determine the percent composition by mass.

MATERIALS

➤ antacid tablet
➤ standardized 0.100 *M* NaOH
➤ standardized 1.00 *M* HCl
➤ 0.100 *M* Na_3PO_4 solution

➤ phenolphthalein indicator
➤ mortar and pestle
➤ 2 burets
➤ filter paper and funnel

PROCEDURE

I. Titration

Step A Obtain an antacid tablet and determine its mass.

Step B Crush the tablet in a mortar with a pestle or place the tablet in a small plastic bag and crush it carefully with a heavy object.

Step C Dissolve the tablet in ~25 mL distilled H_2O. Heat and stir if necessary. Not all of the tablet may dissolve readily.

Step D Add one or two drops of phenolphthalein indicator solution.

Step E Titrate with standardized 1.00 *M* HCl until the pink solution just turns clear. Then add an additional 1.00 mL HCl.

Step F Back titrate with 0.100 *M* NaOH solution until the solution just becomes pink. The faint pink must persist for 30 seconds of vigorous swirling.

II. Gravimetric Analysis

Step A Add ___?___ mL of 0.100 *M* Na_3PO_4 solution to the previously titrated solution. (You need to calculate the stoichiometric amount needed, then double it.) Mix thoroughly.

Step B Mass a dry filter paper, then place it into a funnel. Filter the precipitate.

Step C Transfer the filter paper and precipitate to a watch glass. Place it in the drying oven and leave overnight.

Step D Find the mass of the filter paper and precipitate.

Calculations

Using the results of your titration:

1. Find how many moles of protons must have come from the standardized HCl solution.
2. Find how many moles of hydroxide must have come from standardized NaOH solution.
3. Subtract to find how many moles of OH^- must have come from the $Mg(OH)_2$ tablet.
4. Using stoichiometry, calculate the mass of $Mg(OH)_2$ in the tablet.
5. Calculate the mass percent of $Mg(OH)_2$ in the tablet.

PROCEDURE
(continued)

Using the results of your gravimetric analysis:

6. Determine the mass of $Mg_3(PO_4)_2$ precipitate.
7. Using stoichiometry, calculate the number of moles of Mg^{2+} that must have come from the tablet. Calculate the mass of $Mg(OH)_2$ that must have come from the tablet.
8. Calculate the mass percent of $Mg(OH)_2$ in the tablet.

Post-Lab Questions

1. Which of the following salts is least soluble? Show complete calculations to support your answer.

Compound	K_{sp}
$MgCO_3$	3.5×10^{-8}
MgF_2	3.7×10^{-8}
$Mg(OH)_2$	1.8×10^{-11}
$Mg_3(PO_4)_2$	1.0×10^{-25}
MgC_2O_4	2.5×10^{-13}

Post-Lab Questions *(continued)*

2. Why can you not make a standard molarity NaOH solution directly from dry NaOH?

3. Select an indicator that might be appropriate for a base-to-acid titration.

Name _____ Date _____

Instructor _____ Section _____

Experiment

Analysis of a Volatile Liquid

PURPOSE

- Determine the molecular mass, the density, and the boiling point of an unknown volatile liquid
- Calculate and explain the percent error of the calculations on the volatile liquid
- Determine the applicability of certain techniques for the analysis and identification of various compounds

INTRODUCTION

In the study of chemistry, clues to the identity of a substance are frequently found among its physical characteristics. As you will discover in a number of procedures in this laboratory manual, you can use several of your senses to help you. Although tasting is not used in the chemistry laboratory for safety reasons, your nose *is* an excellent tool. A cautious sniff of a sample, wafted toward your nose by careful fanning of your hand over the substance, can give you a hint. A strong odor might indicate that the substance in your sample is quite volatile. Similarly, using your eyes to ascertain color, viscosity, or translucence can pay off.

A **volatile liquid** is one that can be easily heated to convert it to gaseous form. Here are three techniques for analysis of a volatile liquid.

Molecular Mass The **molecular mass** (or molar mass) of a gas can be calculated using the **Ideal Gas Law**

$$PV = nRT$$

with just one substitution. Because the number of moles n of a substance can be determined by dividing the mass of a sample by its molar mass (MM)

$$n = \frac{g}{MM}$$

the Ideal Gas equation can be reconfigured as

$$PV = \frac{gRT}{MM}$$

Algebraic manipulation then gives you

$$MM = \frac{gRT}{PV}$$

In theory, then, the molar mass of any gas can be determined if only you can measure certain physical parameters: the mass of the sample and its pressure and volume at a certain temperature. As you make these measurements of the physical characteristics of the gaseous form of a volatile liquid, keep in mind this question: Under what circumstances is an ideal gas truly ideal? In other words, how ideal a gas is a volatile liquid?

Density Another physical characteristic that can be measured easily is that of **density**, a comparison of the mass of a sample to the volume it occupies. Using an accurate scale, a *CRC* or other handbook for a bit of research, and a special volumetric flask called a **pycnometer**, you can accurately determine the density of your volatile liquid.

Boiling Point Earlier in your science career, you may have defined the boiling point of a substance as "the temperature at which something changes from liquid to gas." This definition is wholly inadequate for the AP Chemistry student. The **boiling point** represents an equilibrium situation, one in which the rate of change from liquid to gas is matched by that of gas to liquid. The pressure exerted on the surface of the liquid by the atmosphere alters this exchange. In fact, another way to define the same idea is to state that the boiling point is the temperature at which the vapor pressure (liquid becoming gas) is equaled by the atmospheric pressure (gas becoming liquid). You will use this idea to determine accurately the boiling point of the volatile liquid.

Procedure Preview This experiment consists of three separate laboratory analyses, each with its own sets of procedures and materials. Following the completion of these analyses and your collection and organization of data, you will calculate the molecular mass, the density at a certain temperature, and the boiling point at a certain atmospheric pressure of your unknown volatile liquid. At this point, will you be able to conclusively identify it?

I. Molecular Mass of a Volatile Liquid

MATERIALS
> hot plate
> 25-mL Erlenmeyer flask
> large beaker
> gas flask
> Pasteur pipet
> electronic balance
> unknown volatile liquid (from instructor)

PROCEDURE

Step A Start a hot water bath on a hot plate and allow it to come to a rolling boil. The beaker you select must be large enough to accommodate a 25-mL Erlenmeyer flask.

Step B Create a gas flask by cutting a circle of aluminum foil slightly larger than the neck of a 25-mL Erlenmeyer flask. Secure the foil to the flask with a small rubber band and trim away any excess foil. (Alternatively, use composite cork and glass tubing drawn to a point.) Mass the entire apparatus.

Step C Make a tiny hole in the foil with a pushpin.

PROCEDURE
(continued)

Step D Using a Pasteur pipet, squirt through the pinhole enough of the volatile liquid sample to wet completely the bottom of the flask.

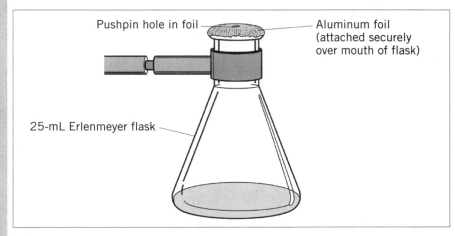

Pushpin hole in foil

Aluminum foil (attached securely over mouth of flask)

25-mL Erlenmeyer flask

Figure 6.1 After transfer of the volatile liquid to the flask, the apparatus is lowered into a boiling water bath until the liquid has vaporized.

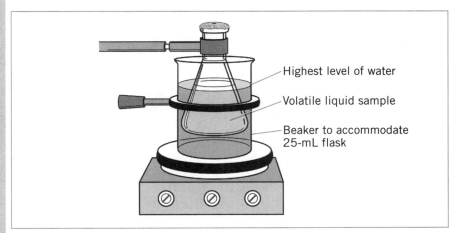

Highest level of water

Volatile liquid sample

Beaker to accommodate 25-mL flask

Figure 6.2 Complete apparatus for determining the molecular mass of a volatile liquid. Be sure no water enters through pinhole.

Step E Using a test tube clamp to hold the apparatus, lower it into the boiling water bath. Do not submerge the apparatus, since water must not enter the pinhole.

Step F When the liquid has vaporized, remove the apparatus from the water bath. While walking toward the electronic balance, dry the outside of the flask with a paper towel. Again, mass the apparatus.

Step G Add another drop or two of the volatile liquid through the pinhole and repeat the process at least three times.

Step H Remove the foil and rubber band. Fill the flask with distilled water and determine the mass. Note the temperature of the water. Using the *CRC*, find the density of water at that temperature. Calculate the actual volume of the flask.

II. Density of a Volatile Liquid

MATERIALS

➤ pycnometer *(see Appendix D on page 142)*
➤ Pasteur pipet
➤ Bunsen burner
➤ volatile liquid (from instructor)

PROCEDURE

Step A To create a pycnometer, use a piece of Pasteur pipet (or soft glass tubing) approximately 2 cm long. Seal one end completely in a Bunsen burner flame. Nearly seal the other end, but leave an opening 3–4 millimeters wide, just enough to accommodate the *tip* of a Pasteur pipet.

Step B Mass the clean, dry pycnometer.

Step C Obtain a sample of volatile liquid in a Pasteur pipet. Fill the pycnometer carefully with volatile liquid by inserting the tip of the Pasteur pipet, then gently squeezing the bulb to achieve a flow. Slowly remove the tip and continue to squeeze the bulb. Do not allow a bubble to form inside the pycnometer.

Step D Dry the outside of the pycnometer and find its mass.

Step E Remove the volatile liquid from the pycnometer with the Pasteur pipet. Drive any excess liquid from the pycnometer with a gentle flame. (***Caution:*** Be careful not to crack the pycnometer. Do not launch the tiny rocket across the room!)

Step F Fill the pycnometer with distilled water and mass it. Calculate the volume of the pycnometer. Refer to the *CRC* or other handbook to find the accurate density of distilled water at the current temperature of your laboratory.

III. Boiling Point of a Volatile Liquid

MATERIALS

➤ capillary tube
➤ Bunsen burner and hot plate
➤ thermometer
➤ transparent tape
➤ 100 × 13 mm (or smaller) test tube
➤ 50-mL beaker
➤ volatile liquid (from instructor)

PROCEDURE

Step A Create three or four very tiny test tubes (T^3) by breaking a capillary tube into three or four pieces, then sealing one end in a Bunsen burner flame.

Step B Use transparent tape to strap a small test tube onto a thermometer (or temperature probe).

PROCEDURE
(continued)

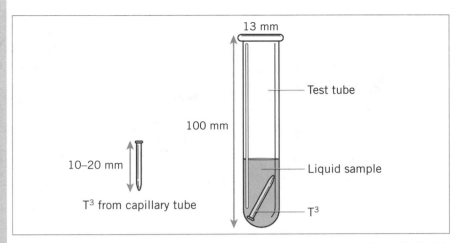

Figure 6.3 A micro-test tube is dropped open-end down into a sample of volatile liquid.

Step C Pour a sample of the volatile liquid into the test tube. Drop one T^3 into the liquid, open end down. The T^3 should be submerged.

Step D Start a water bath on a hotplate. Adjust the hot plate so that the temperature of the water rises slowly. Insert the test tube/thermometer apparatus into the beaker so that the entire sample of volatile liquid is below the surface of the water bath.

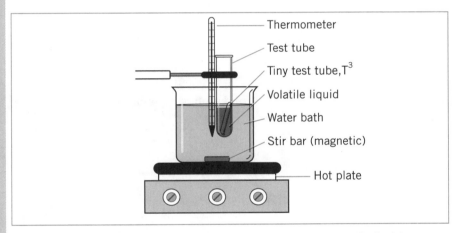

Figure 6.4 Apparatus for determining boiling point of a volatile liquid.

Step E Observe the open end of the T^3 until a rapid, steady stream of small bubbles is emitted into the liquid. Then remove the entire water bath and apparatus from the hot plate.

Step F Observe carefully the end of the T^3. When the stream of bubbles slows, then suddenly reverses direction back into the T^3, observe the temperature. Repeat this process with the remaining T^3. (There is no need to remove the spent T^3 from the liquid.)

Calculations

1. Present all your data in tabular form.
2. Calculate *MM* of the volatile liquid.
3. Calculate the density of the volatile liquid.
4. Record the boiling point of the volatile liquid.

1. Obtain the identity of your sample from the instructor. Find in the *CRC* its *MM*, density, and boiling point. Calculate your percent error.

2. Which of the three techniques was closest to standard? Why? Could you conclusively identify the liquid using these techniques? Explain.

_____

_____

_____

_____

_____

3. Explain the fundamental ideas of the Ideal Gas Model. Do you expect the sample of volatile liquid to behave ideally? Why or why not?

_____

_____

_____

_____

_____

4. Could you use these techniques to analyze the *MM*, bp, and density of a sample of gallium?

_____

octane?

_____

butane?

_____

water?

_____

For each, explain why or why not.

5. What are the measurement errors for the *MM* technique? How significant is their contribution to any overall error? What do you see as the major source of error in this technique? Explain.

_____

_____

_____

_____

_____

Name _____   Date _____

Instructor _____   Section _____

Experiment

7   Job's Method of Continuous Variation

PURPOSE

- Determine the stoichiometry of a chemical reaction experimentally
- Determine the chemical formula of a precipitate
- Determine the oxidation state of an ion in solution

INTRODUCTION

How can the stoichiometry of a chemical reaction or the formula of a compound be determined experimentally? It can be done using **Job's Method of Continuous Variation**, which keeps the *total* number of moles of reactants *constant* throughout a series of mixtures of reactants, but varies the mole fraction of each reactant from mixture to mixture. Certain specific measurements are then taken for each of the mixtures. Because the maximum change will occur when the mole fraction of the reactants is closest to the actual stoichiometric mole ratio, both the formula of the product and the reactant stoichiometry can be determined using this approach. Specifically, by measuring the change in temperature, the pH, the absorbance, and the mass of precipitate formed for each reaction mixture, and by graphing these measurements versus mole fraction, one can determine the mole fraction for each reactant that produces the maximum change.

Figure 7.1

By measuring changes in various states of a solution in relation to the mole fraction of its reactants, one can find the mole fraction that produces maximum change. This graph relates mass of precipitate formed to mole fraction.

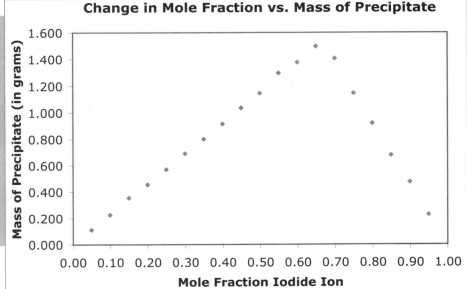

Change in Mole Fraction vs. Mass of Precipitate

Keep in mind that the maximum change will occur when each reactant is a *limiting* reactant. So, the graph of mole fraction versus change will show a region starting when the mole fraction of this reactant is zero and increasing as the mole fraction of this reactant increases until the stoichiometric mole ratio of reactants is reached. In this region, the slope of the change will be positive, and the limiting reactant will be the reactant being graphed. When the maximum change is reached, the other reactant becomes the limiting reactant, and the magnitude of the change drops, resulting in a negative slope in this region. Where the change is biphasic, there will be a region with a positive slope for the mole-fraction range in which the reactant graphed is the limiting reactant, and a region with a negative slope for the range in which the reactant graphed is in excess. The point at which these lines intersect is the experimental value for the mole fraction of the reactant that produces maximum change when both reactants are limiting reactants. The ratio of mole fractions of ion in this compound will be used to determine the chemical formula of the product and the stoichiometric ratio. The ratio of these mole fractions is the stoichiometric ratio of the reactants in the chemical reaction. The oxidation number of the reacting ion can then also be determined.

Pre-Lab Questions

A student was trying to determine the formula of a lead iodide precipitate by mixing solutions of 0.1 *M* potassium iodide with 0.1 *M* lead nitrate. The experimental data are given in this table.

Volume of 0.1 *M* potassium iodide (mL)	Volume of 0.1 *M* lead nitrate (mL)	Mass of precipitate formed (g)
1.0	19.0	0.115
2.0	18.0	0.230
3.0	17.0	0.359
4.0	16.0	0.460
5.0	15.0	0.575
6.0	14.0	0.695
7.0	13.0	0.805
8.0	12.0	0.920
9.0	11.0	1.040
10.0	10.0	1.150
11.0	9.0	1.300
12.0	8.0	1.380
13.0	7.0	1.500
14.0	6.0	1.410
15.0	5.0	1.150
16.0	4.0	0.924
17.0	3.0	0.682
18.0	2.0	0.479
19.0	1.0	0.231

1. **a.** Why is there no data for the mixture of 20.0 mL of lead nitrate with 0.0 mL of potassium iodide or for the 20.0 mL of potassium iodide with 0.0 mL of lead nitrate?

_____

_____

b. What would the mass of the precipitate be if those data points were collected?

_____

_____

2. The data in the preceding table have been converted to mole fraction of iodide ion, and the mole fraction of iodide ion has been plotted versus the mass of precipitate formed in Figure 7.1. Use the graph in Figure 7.1 to estimate the stoichiometric ratio of lead ion to iodide ion by drawing a best-fit line for the data with a positive slope and a separate best-fit line for the data with a negative slope. Drop a perpendicular to the x-axis from the intersection point of these best-fit lines to determine the mole fraction of the iodide ion needed to form the maximum mass of precipitate.

a. What is the mole fraction of lead nitrate at this point?

_____

_____

_____

b. What is the mole fraction of potassium iodide at this point?

_____

_____

_____

c. Determine the stoichiometric ratio between these ions by taking the ratio of the mole fractions you found in questions 2a and 2b.

_____

_____

_____

d. Write the formula for the precipitate.

_____

_____

e. Write a balanced net-ionic equation for the reaction that forms this precipitate.

_____

_____

Procedure Preview In the procedural methods that follow, an exothermic reaction between aqueous solutions of sodium hydroxide and a copper ion of unknown oxidation state will be investigated. Because this reaction is a precipitation reaction, you will also measure the height of the precipitate in each test tube after it settles overnight. These experimental data will not only determine the stoichiometry of the reaction, but they will also be used to determine the formula of the precipitate and the oxidation number of the copper ion:

$$Cu^{x+}_{(aq)} + x\,OH^-_{(aq)} \rightarrow Cu(OH)_{x(s)}$$

Note: Methods 1, 2, and 3 use identical procedures to make the sample solutions, so the same samples produced during Method 1 can later be analyzed using Method 2, where the pH of each sample is measured, and then again using Method 3, where the absorbance at 635 nanometers (nm) is measured with a colorimeter. Similarly, Methods 4 and 5 use identical procedures to make sample solutions, so the samples whose temperature change is measured during Method 4 can be used to measure the mass of precipitate formed in the reaction by filtration in Method 5.

Method 1: Height of Precipitate and Qualitative Observations

In this experiment, you will mix known volumes of sodium hydroxide solution with known volumes of a copper ion solution, keeping the total volumes of solutions mixed to 10.00 mL. After thoroughly mixing the reactants and allowing the precipitate to settle overnight, you will take careful observations of the solid and the solution and measure the height of the precipitate. By graphing the mole fraction of hydroxide ion versus the height of the precipitate, you will be able to determine the ratio of mole fractions of the reactants ($\chi_{copper\ ion}$ and χ_{OH^-}). The ratio of these mole fractions ($\chi_{copper\ ion}/\chi_{OH^-}$) can be used to determine the stoichiometric ratio of the reactants and then the formula of the hydroxide product and the oxidation state of the copper ion.

MATERIALS

- ➤ two 50-mL burets (or two 10.00-mL graduated pipets)
- ➤ standardized 1 *M* sodium hydroxide solution
- ➤ copper sulfate solution of same molarity
- ➤ test tubes and test tube rack
- ➤ stirring rods
- ➤ ruler

PROCEDURE

Step A Label thirteen test tubes sequentially from 1 through 13. Use a clean and rinsed buret (or graduated pipet) to deliver the volume of copper ion solution to each test tube. Record the exact volume added in your data table. Repeat the following steps for each of the 13 test tubes.

Step B Using a clean and rinsed buret (or graduated pipet), deliver the appropriate volume of standardized hydroxide solution to the test tube, being careful not to contaminate the buret (or pipet tip). Record the exact volume of hydroxide solution added.

PROCEDURE
(continued)

control →

control →

Test Tube #	Volume copper ion (mL)	Volume OH⁻ (mL)
1	0.00	10.00
2	1.00	9.00
3	2.00	8.00
4	2.50	7.50
5	3.00	7.00
6	3.33	6.67
7	4.00	6.00
8	5.00	5.00
9	6.00	4.00
10	7.00	3.00
11	8.00	2.00
12	9.00	1.00
13	10.00	0.00

Step C Stir the mixture carefully with a stirring rod and then cover the test tube with a rubber stopper.

Step D Let the precipitate settle for a period of time, as directed by your teacher.

Step E Remove the test tube from the rack and rest its bottom on the lab bench. Hold the test tube straight upright.

Step F Measure the height of the precipitate. Repeat for each sample.

Step G Arrange the test tubes side-by-side in the rack in order of increasing volume of hydroxide added. Placing a sheet of white paper behind your samples, carefully observe both the precipitate and the **supernatant**—that is, the solution on top of the solid. Record these observations in your data table.

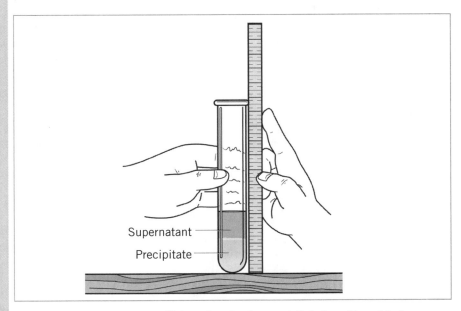

Figure 7.2 Be sure to allow sufficient time for the precipitate to settle out before measuring and recording.

Calculations (Method 1)

1. Present all your data in tabular form.
2. Calculate the mole fraction of both the copper ion and the hydroxide ion in each sample.
3. Using your observations, list the test tubes in which the copper ion is the reactant in excess.
4. Using your answers to calculations 1–3, predict the stoichiometric ratio of the chemical reaction.
5. Graph the mole fraction of copper ion versus the height of precipitate. Draw a line of best fit for both the positive and negative slope regions. Drop a perpendicular from the intersection point to the x-axis to find the mole fraction of the copper ion that produces maximum change.
6. Use your answer to calculation 5 to determine the mole fraction of hydroxide ion at the intersection point. Use these mole fractions to determine the formula of the ionic compound that precipitated in the reaction.
7. Determine the stoichiometric ratio of copper ion to hydroxide ion for this reaction.
8. Write a balanced net-ionic reaction equation for the precipitation reaction.

Method 2: pH

This method uses the same procedure for steps A–D as in Method 1, so the samples sealed in the test tubes after data collection in Method 1 may be used.

MATERIALS

➤ two 50-mL burets (or two 10.00-mL graduated pipets)
➤ standardized 1 M sodium hydroxide solution
➤ copper sulfate solution of same molarity
➤ test tubes and test tube rack
➤ stirring rods
➤ pH probe

PROCEDURE

Step A Label thirteen test tubes sequentially from 1 through 13. Use a clean and rinsed buret (or graduated pipet) to deliver the volume of copper ion solution to each test tube. Record the exact volumes added in your data table. Repeat the following steps for each of the 13 test tubes.

Test Tube #	Volume copper ion (mL)	Volume OH⁻ (mL)
1	0.00	10.00
2	1.00	9.00
3	2.00	8.00
4	2.50	7.50
5	3.00	7.00
6	3.33	6.67
7	4.00	6.00
8	5.00	5.00
9	6.00	4.00
10	7.00	3.00
11	8.00	2.00
12	9.00	1.00
13	10.00	0.00

PROCEDURE
(continued)

Step B Using a clean and rinsed buret (or graduated pipet), deliver the appropriate volume of standardized hydroxide solution to the test tube, being careful not to contaminate the buret (or pipet tip). Record the exact volumes of hydroxide solution added.

Step C Stir each mixture carefully with a stirring rod and then cover the test tubes with rubber stoppers.

Step D Let the precipitate settle for a period of time, as directed by your teacher.

Step E Follow your teacher's directions to standardize your pH probe.

Step F Without disturbing the precipitate, carefully place the pH probe in the test tube so the glass bulb on the bottom is covered by the solution.

Step G Allow the pH reading to become constant. Then record the pH reading in the data table.

Step H Repeat for each sample.

Calculations (Method 2)

1. Present all of your data in tabular form.
2. Calculate the mole fraction of both the copper ion and the hydroxide ion in each sample.
3. Graph mole fraction of copper ion versus pH.
4. The graph you made for calculation 3 is called a **titration curve**. Follow the instructions outlined in Experiment 10, Method 3, on page(s) 71–79 to determine the equivalence point on the titration curve. Your instructor will tell you which specific approach outlined there to follow to determine the equivalence point on your titration curve graph.
5. Using your answers from calculation 4, calculate the mole fraction of hydroxide ion at that point. Then use the ratio of mole fractions of copper ion to hydroxide ion to determine the formula of the ionic compound that precipitated in the reaction.
6. Determine the stoichiometric ratio of copper ion to hydroxide ion for this reaction.
7. Write a balanced net-ionic reaction equation for the precipitation reaction.

Method 3: Absorbance at 635 Nanometers

This method uses the same procedure for steps A–D as in Method 1, so the samples sealed in the test tubes after data collection in Method 1 can be used.

MATERIALS

➤ two 50-mL burets (or two 10.00-mL graduated pipets)
➤ standardized 1 *M* sodium hydroxide solution
➤ copper sulfate solution of same molarity
➤ test tubes and test tube rack
➤ stirring rods
➤ colorimeter (or Spectronic 20 spectrophotometer)
➤ cuvettes
➤ transfer pipets

PROCEDURE

Step A Label thirteen test tubes sequentially from 1 through 13. Use a clean and rinsed buret (or graduated pipet) to deliver the volume of copper ion solution to each test tube. Record the exact volumes added in your data table. Repeat the following steps for each of the 13 test tubes.

Test Tube #	Volume copper ion (mL)	Volume OH⁻ (mL)
1	0.00	10.00
2	1.00	9.00
3	2.00	8.00
4	2.50	7.50
5	3.00	7.00
6	3.33	6.67
7	4.00	6.00
8	5.00	5.00
9	6.00	4.00
10	7.00	3.00
11	8.00	2.00
12	9.00	1.00
13	10.00	0.00

Step B Use a clean and rinsed buret (or graduated pipet) to deliver the appropriate volume of standardized hydroxide solution to the test tube, being careful not to contaminate the buret (or pipet tip). Record the exact volume of hydroxide solution added.

Step C Stir each mixture carefully with a stirring rod, then cover the test tubes with a rubber stopper.

Step D Let the precipitate settle for a period of time, as directed by your teacher.

Step E Be sure your spectrophotometer is warmed up. Follow the teacher's directions to zero your colorimeter (or Spectronic 20) at 635 nm.

Step F Without disturbing the precipitate, carefully remove a sample from the test tube, using a transfer pipet, and place in cuvette. Be sure to fill the cuvette with the appropriate volume of sample. (Ask your teacher what to do if you do not have sufficient sample to fill the cuvette. You will be told how to perform a careful dilution using distilled water and how to correct the measured absorbance for any dilution.)

Step G Be sure no solid is in the sample, then remove all air bubbles. Wipe the outside of cuvette with a damp paper towel to remove any fingerprints or dirt.

Step H Place the cuvette in the colorimeter (or Spectronic 20) and close the cover. Read absorbance at 635 nm and record in data table.

Step I Repeat for each sample.

PROCEDURE
(continued)

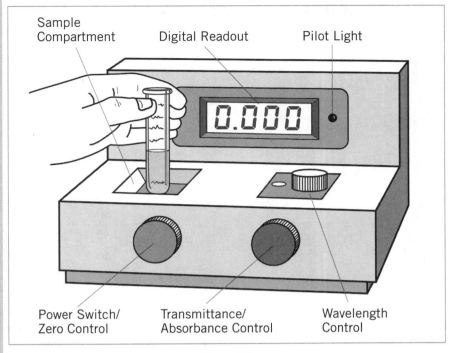

Figure 7.3

Calculations (Method 3)

1. Present all of your data in tabular form.
2. Calculate the mole fraction of both the copper ion and the hydroxide ion in each sample.
3. Graph mole fraction of copper ion versus absorbance.
4. Carefully analyze this graph to determine the mole fraction of copper ion when there is a significant change in the absorbance readings.
5. Using your answer to calculation 4, calculate the mole fraction of hydroxide ion at that point, and then use the ratio of mole fractions of copper ion to hydroxide ion to determine the formula of the ionic compound that precipitated in the reaction.
6. Determine the stoichiometric ratio of copper ion to hydroxide ion for this reaction.
7. Write a balanced net-ionic reaction equation for the precipitation reaction.

Method 4: Temperature Change

MATERIALS

➤ two 50-mL graduated cylinders
➤ two 25-mL graduated cylinders
➤ standardized 1 *M* sodium hydroxide solution
➤ copper sulfate solution of same molarity
➤ polystyrene coffee cup placed in 250-mL beaker
➤ thermometer (or temperature probe)
➤ stirring rod

Step A Use the appropriate graduated cylinder to measure the volumes of hydroxide ion solution. Record the exact volumes in the data table.

Volume copper ion (mL)	Volume OH⁻ (mL)
0.0	50.0
5.0	45.0
10.0	40.0
15.0	35.0
20.0	30.0
25.0	25.0
30.0	20.0
35.0	15.0
40.0	10.0
45.0	5.0
50.0	0.0

Step B Measure the initial temperature of hydroxide ion solution. Record the initial temperature in the data table.

Step C Rinse the thermometer with distilled water and dry.

Step D Use the appropriate graduated cylinder to measure copper ion solution and pour sample into the coffee cup/beaker apparatus. Record the exact volume added in your data table.

Step E Add the thermometer and monitor solution temperature until unchanged for 1 minute. Record initial temperature in data table.

Step F Pour hydroxide solution into the copper ion solution and stir while constantly reading the thermometer. Keep stirring and reading until the maximum temperature is reached. Record the maximum temperature in the data table.

Step G Follow the teacher's instructions about where to place the used sample waste.

Step H Rinse the coffee cup, thermometer, and stirring rod with distilled water and pat dry.

Step I Repeat all steps above for the next set of solution volumes until all samples are mixed. Save samples to use in Method 5.

Calculations (Method 4)

1. Present all of your data in tabular form.
2. Calculate the mole fraction of both the copper ion and the hydroxide ion in each sample.
3. Calculate change in temperature (ΔT) for each copper ion sample.
4. Graph the mole fraction of copper ion versus ΔT. Draw a line of best fit for both the positive and the negative slope regions. Drop a perpendicular from the intersection point to the x-axis to determine the mole fraction of the copper ion that produces the maximum change.
5. Use your answer to calculation 4 to determine the mole fraction of hydroxide ion at the intersection point. Use these mole fractions to determine the formula of the ionic compound that precipitated in the reaction.
6. Determine the stoichiometric ratio of copper ion to hydroxide ion for this reaction.
7. Write a balanced net-ionic reaction equation for the precipitation reaction.

Method 5: Mass of Precipitate

MATERIALS

➤ two 50-mL graduated cylinders
➤ two 25-mL graduated cylinders
➤ standardized 1 *M* sodium hydroxide solution
➤ copper sulfate solution of same molarity
➤ beakers
➤ stirring rod
➤ filter paper and funnels
➤ ring stands and rings
➤ electronic balance

PROCEDURE

Step A Use the appropriate graduated cylinder to measure the appropriate volume of copper ion solution and pour into beaker. Record the exact volume in the data table.

Volume copper ion (mL)	Volume OH⁻ (mL)
0.0	50.0
5.0	45.0
10.0	40.0
15.0	35.0
20.0	30.0
25.0	25.0
30.0	20.0
35.0	15.0
40.0	10.0
45.0	5.0
50.0	0.0

Step B Use the appropriate graduated cylinder to measure hydroxide ion solution and record the exact volume in your data table.

Step C Pour hydroxide solution into the copper ion solution and stir. Stir thoroughly for about one minute to allow precipitate to form.

Step D Repeat steps A–C for the other samples.

Step E Label 9 filter papers and measure the mass of each. Record each mass in your data table.

Step F Set up ring stand, ring, and funnel; then place a pre-massed filter paper in each funnel.

Step G Stir one sample completely to resuspend the precipitate, then pour the suspension into filter paper.

Step H After all of the sample has been poured onto the filter paper, rinse the beaker with distilled water and pour the distilled water onto the filter paper.

Step I Repeat Steps G and H for each sample.

Step J Remove the filter paper from the funnel, place it on a watch glass, and allow it to dry in a drying oven.

Step K Measure the mass of the precipitate and filter paper and record. Repeat for each sample.

Step L Follow the teacher's instructions about where to place and dispose of filtrate waste.

Calculations (Method 5)

1. Present all of your data in tabular form.
2. Calculate the mole fraction of both the copper ion and the hydroxide ion in each sample.
3. Calculate the mass of precipitate formed from each copper ion sample.
4. Graph the mole fraction of copper ion versus mass of precipitate. Draw a line of best fit for both the positive and the negative slope regions. Drop a perpendicular from the intersection point to the *x*-axis to determine the mole fraction of the copper ion that produces the maximum change.
5. Use your answer to calculation 4 to determine the mole fraction of hydroxide ion at the intersection point. Use these mole fractions to determine the formula of the ionic compound that precipitated in the reaction.
6. Determine the stoichiometric ratio of copper ion to hydroxide ion for this reaction.
7. Write a balanced net-ionic reaction equation for the precipitation reaction.

Post-Lab Questions

1. Can the stoichiometric ratio be determined by the colors of the resulting supernatants? Explain.

_____

_____

_____

_____

_____

_____

_____

_____

_____

_____

_____

_____

_____

_____

_____

Post-Lab Questions *(continued)*

2. Could the oxidation state of the copper ion be determined by looking at the solution? Explain.

3. Would any of these methods work to determine the reaction stoichiometry for a reaction between the hydroxide ion and the zinc ion? If yes, which methods could you use and why would they work?

Post-Lab Questions *(continued)*

4. Could the graphs use the mole fraction of hydroxide ion instead of the mole fraction of copper ion to determine the reaction stoichiometry? If no, explain why not. If yes, explain how the shape of the graphs would change.

Name _____   Date _____

Instructor _____   Section _____

Experiment

Finding the Mass Percent of Acetic Acid in Vinegar

PURPOSE

- Determine the mass percent and molarity of acetic (ethanoic) acid in household vinegar
- Standardize sodium hydroxide solution using a primary standard as a reference
- Compare two titration methods and their results with data on manufacturer's label

INTRODUCTION

"Vinegar is good wine gone bad," quipped Alton Brown, the TV food show host and science buff. Vinegar, its name derived from the old French word *vinaigre*—from the roots *vin* (wine) and *aigre* (sour)—is a dilute solution of acetic (ethanoic) acid, CH_3COOH or $HC_2H_3O_2$, a weak monoprotic acid. The acidity in vinegar is reduced by addition of water, so that the final acidity typically ranges from 3–7%, depending on the type of vinegar. Rice wine vinegar may have a 3% acidity, while red wine vinegars contain up to 7% acetic acid. The different varieties of vinegar also vary in their color: distilled white vinegar is clear and colorless with a 5% acidity, while balsamic vinegar is dark brown and has higher acidity.

Procedure Preview   In this experiment, you will standardize a 0.5 M NaOH solution using a **primary standard**. A primary standard is a compound that is extremely pure and stable. Therefore, a known amount can be measured by mass and used with confidence to react with another compound or ion in a known reaction. The primary standard serves as a reference during a titration to help determine the actual concentration of some ion or compound in the solution being standardized. Potassium hydrogen phthalate ("KHP"), $KHC_8H_4O_4$, which is a weak, monoprotic acid, will be used as the primary standard since it reacts to neutralize sodium hydroxide in the reaction whose net ionic equation is:

$$HC_8H_4O_4^-{}_{(aq)} + OH^-{}_{(aq)} \rightarrow H_2O_{(l)} + C_8H_4O_4^{2-}{}_{(aq)}$$

You will then use this standardized solution to titrate a vinegar sample of known mass.

$$CH_3COOH_{(aq)} + OH^-{}_{(aq)} \rightarrow CH_3COO^-{}_{(aq)} + H_2O_{(l)}$$

The data collected from this titration will be used to determine the molarity of acetic acid as well as the percent by mass of acetic acid in that type of vinegar. These results can then be compared with values printed on the vinegar label.

1. During storage, solid sodium hydroxide can become contaminated when it reacts with carbon dioxide gas from the atmosphere. Write the balanced net-ionic equation for this reaction.

2. A student wanted to make 0.75 liter of a 0.250 M solution of sodium hydroxide by diluting a 0.750 M standardized sodium hydroxide solution. Calculate the volume of the concentrated solution the student would need to use to make this dilute solution. What volume of water must be added? Assume volumes are additive.

3. The student then used the 0.250 M solution to titrate 0.0500 L of a phosphoric acid sample. The student's data were:

Initial buret reading: 14.00 mL

Final buret reading: 26.50 mL

   a. Write a balanced chemical equation describing this reaction.

   b. Calculate the concentration of this sample in moles per liter.

4. Once a bottle of vinegar is opened and used regularly, it loses its acidity over time. Can you remember the smell of vinegar? Explain why the acidity of vinegar decreases over time when the bottle is used regularly.

_____

_____

_____

_____

_____

_____

_____

_____

_____

_____

_____

Titration Method Using a 50-mL Buret

MATERIALS

- 50-mL buret
- buret clamp and buret stand
- two 125-mL Erlenmeyer flasks
- white paper
- phenolphthalein solution
- ~0.5 M NaOH
- potassium hydrogen phthalate
- distilled water
- 25-mL graduated cylinder
- balance
- vinegar sample(s)
- volumetric pipet

PROCEDURE

I. Standardization of sodium hydroxide solution

Step A Measure the masses of two clean, dry 125-mL Erlenmeyer flasks.

Step B Add about 1 gram of potassium hydrogen phthalate to each flask, recording the exact mass added to each flask.

Step C Add about 25 mL of distilled water to each flask and swirl to dissolve the potassium hydrogen phthalate.

Step D Add 2 drops of phenolphthalein solution to each flask and mix by swirling.

Step E Fill a clean and dry 50-mL buret with standardized NaOH solution and drain some of the solution into a waste beaker to remove air from tip.

Step F Record the initial volume of the base to 0.01 mL.

Step G Place the first Erlenmeyer flask on white paper and titrate the acetic acid in the vinegar to the endpoint, noted by the faint pink color, then record final volume of base to 0.01 mL.

Step H Repeat Step G for the second sample.

II. Analysis of vinegar sample

Step A Measure the masses of two clean, dry 125-mL Erlenmeyer flasks.

Step B Add 10.00 mL of vinegar to each flask, using a volumetric pipet, then record the exact volume used. Mass each flask and vinegar again.

Step C Using a graduated cylinder, add about 15 mL of distilled water to each flask.

Step D Add 2 drops of phenolphthalein solution to each flask and mix by swirling.

Step E Fill a clean and dry 50-mL buret with standardized NaOH solution and drain some of the solution into a waste beaker to remove air from the tip.

Step F Record actual concentration of NaOH solution and initial volume of the base to 0.01 mL.

Step G Place the Erlenmeyer flask on white paper and titrate the acetic acid in the vinegar to the endpoint noted by the faint pink color.

Step H Record the final volume.

Step I Dispose of solution as directed by your teacher.

Step J Repeat Steps F–I for the second sample.

PROCEDURE
(continued)

Calculations

1. Calculate the moles of potassium hydrogen phthalate in each sample titrated.
2. Calculate the molarity of sodium hydroxide for each sample, then calculate the average molarity of sodium hydroxide.
3. Calculate the mass of vinegar in each sample titrated.
4. Calculate the moles of acetic acid in each vinegar sample using your titration data.
5. Calculate the mass of acetic acid in each vinegar sample.
6. Calculate the percent by mass of acetic acid in each vinegar sample.
7. Compare your results to the value stated by the manufacturer on the label of the vinegar container. Calculate the percent error in your results for each vinegar sample.
8. Calculate the molarity of acetic acid in each vinegar sample.

Titration Method Using a 2-mL Microburet

MATERIALS

➤ 2-mL microburet *(see Appendix B)*
➤ buret clamp and buret stand
➤ 24-well microplate
➤ white paper
➤ phenolphthalein solution
➤ potassium hydrogen phthalate solution
(~9 g potassium hydrogen phthalate/250.0 mL solution)

➤ ~0.5 *M* NaOH
➤ microstir bars *(see Appendix C)*
➤ magnetic stirrer
➤ vinegar sample(s)

PROCEDURE

I. Preparing the microwell plate

Step A Measure the mass of a clean, dry 24-well microplate.

Step B Add a micro-stir bar to a numbered well and measure the mass of the microwell plate. Record both the mass and the well number.

Step C Repeat step B, putting a stir bar in a different well.

Step D Add 1.00 mL of vinegar from buret into first well and then record the mass.

Step E Repeat step D for second well.

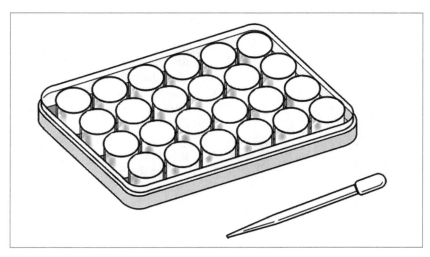

Figure 8.1 For experiments demanding a series or comparison of reactions, a well-plate and microburet or small-volume pipet may be most suitable.

II. Standardization of sodium hydroxide solution

Step A Add 1.00 mL of potassium hydrogen phthalate solution to two different microwells, recording each well number and exact volume added to it. Also **record exact concentration of this solution**.

Step B Record the concentration of the potassium hydrogen phthalate solution.

Step C Add 1 drop of phenolphthalein solution and micro-stir bar to each well.

Step D Place a sheet of white paper on a magnetic stir plate, then place microwell plate on magnetic stirrer with well to be used in center of plate. Turn on magnetic stirrer so that the micro-stir bar slowly rotates and mixes the vinegar sample in the well to be titrated.

Step E Fill microburet with the sodium hydroxide solution to be standardized and rinse microburet twice with the sodium hydroxide solution.

Step F Record actual concentration of sodium hydroxide solution and initial volume of the base to the 0.001 mL.

Step G Titrate sample to the endpoint noted when phenolphthalein turns light pink. Record final volume.

Step H Repeat Steps D–G for the second sample of potassium hydrogen phthalate.

III. Analysis of vinegar sample

Step A Add 1 drop of phenolphthalein solution to each well containing vinegar.

Step B Place a sheet of white paper on a magnetic stir plate, then place the microwell plate on a magnetic stirrer with the well to be used in center of plate. Turn on the magnetic stirrer so that the micro-stir bar slowly rotates and mixes the vinegar sample in the well to be titrated.

Step C Fill microburet with standardized sodium hydroxide solution and rinse tip.

Step D Record actual concentration of sodium hydroxide solution and initial volume of the base to the 0.001 mL.

Step E Titrate sample to the endpoint noted when phenolphthalein turns light pink. Record final volume.

Step F Repeat Steps B–E for second vinegar sample.

Calculations

1. Calculate the moles of potassium hydrogen phthalate in each sample titrated.
2. Calculate the molarity of sodium hydroxide for each sample, then calculate the average molarity of sodium hydroxide.
3. Calculate the mass of vinegar in each sample titrated.
4. Calculate the moles of acetic acid in each vinegar sample using your titration data.
5. Calculate the mass of acetic acid in each vinegar sample.
6. Calculate the percent by mass of acetic acid in each vinegar sample.
7. Compare your results to the value stated by the manufacturer on the label of the vinegar container. Calculate the percent error in your results for each vinegar sample.
8. Calculate the average molarity of acetic acid for each type of vinegar analyzed.

Post-Lab Questions

1. Compare your average percent by mass of acetic acid to the value printed on the label of the vinegar bottle. Comment briefly on any similarities and differences.

2. Can this procedure be used to determine the acidity of dark brown balsamic vinegar? Explain your answer.

3. In the procedure using the 50-mL buret, you added about 15 mL of distilled water to the flask. Does the exact volume of water added affect your experimental results? Explain your answer.

Post-Lab Questions *(continued)*

4. In the procedure using the 50-mL buret, you measured the mass of potassium hydrogen phthalate added and dissolved this mass in distilled water. What would happen to the calculated mass percent of acetic acid in vinegar if some solid potassium hydrogen phthalate remained undissolved when the indicator turned pink and you ended your titration? Explain in detail.

5. In the microtitration experiment, the mass of the microwell plate and microstir bar was measured after the mass of the microwell plate was measured, but before any vinegar sample was added. If a student forgot to measure this mass, how would the percent by mass of acetic acid in vinegar be impacted? Explain your answer in detail.

Name _____   Date _____

Instructor _____   Section _____

Experiment

Analysis by Redox Titration

PURPOSE

- Standardize a $KMnO_4$ solution using iron(II) ("ferrous") ammonium sulfate as a standard
- Determine the concentration (mass percent and molarity) of a preparation of H_2O_2
- Calculate the mass percent of iron in a consumer iron supplement

INTRODUCTION

One common reaction type in chemistry is **oxidation-reduction**. It involves the transfer of electrons from one species to another. A species undergoes **oxidation** when a loss of electrons occurs. A substance undergoes **reduction** when it gains electrons. This process always occurs in pairs because it is a transfer from one species to another. A reducing agent is a species that causes reduction by donating electrons to another species, causing its oxidation number to decrease. Therefore, a reducing agent is itself always oxidized and its oxidation number is always increased. An oxidizing agent causes oxidation in another species by accepting that species' electrons, allowing oxidation (and increase of oxidation number) of the other species. Therefore, an oxidizing agent is itself always reduced and its oxidation number decreases.

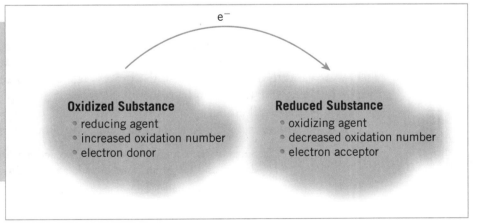

Figure 9.1

Whereas in acid-base reactions protons are transferred from one substance to another, in redox reactions electrons are transferred.

There are two general types of oxidation-reduction, or **redox**, equations. One signal of a redox reaction is the presence of an elemental form as a reactant. Other redox reactions occur in solution and may involve ionic forms. Frequently they involve common oxidizing agents such as the permanganate, chromate, or dichromate ions. In each of these, the metal cation has increased its oxidation number to or near its maximum. For example, manganese has lost seven electrons (the $4s^2$ and $3d^5$ electrons) to attain $+7$. Therefore, the manganese can only be reduced, gaining electrons from and causing oxidation of another species. These reactions are usually specified as being in acidic or basic (alkaline) solution.

The **balancing** of a redox equation is not done by conservation of mass or by counting numbers of atoms. Rather, the redox reaction is described by balancing the loss of electrons from one species and the gain of electrons from another. Because there is only one transfer of electrons in the reaction, the loss and gain of electrons must match. To facilitate the bookkeeping of electron transfers, **oxidation numbers (ON)** are assigned to each atom represented in each species; the oxidation number should not be thought of as the same as the actual charge in the compound or ion. Rules for assigning oxidation numbers can be summarized as follows:

➤ Atoms in elemental form have zero as an oxidation number. Thus, atoms in Fe, F_2, P_4, or S_8 all have an ON of 0.

➤ Monoatomic ions have an oxidation number equal to the charge on the ion. Hence, the ON of chloride is -1 while that of sulfide is -2.

➤ When combined with other atoms, atoms of group 1A (alkali metals) always have an ON of $+1$; atoms of group 2A (alkaline earth metals) always have an ON of $+2$.

➤ Combined oxygen always has an ON of -2 (except for peroxide or when combined with fluorine).

➤ Combined hydrogen always has an ON of $+1$ (except for hydrides).

➤ Combined fluorine always has an ON of -1.

The ON of any other atom must be determined from its context. The sum of all ON within a compound must be zero (thus the ON of sulfur in H_2SO_4 must be $+6$). Within a polyatomic ion, the sum of ON must equal the overall charge on the ion (thus the ON of phosphorus in PO_4^{3-} must be $+5$ because $(-3) = 4(-2) + (ON\ of\ P)$).

Troubleshooting To complete this and many other labs properly, it is crucially important to learn the definitions of oxidation-reduction chemistry carefully and thoroughly. Because the process is a directional transfer of electrons, getting one definition backward will cause all other processes to be reversed, and chaos will ensue!

Here is a technique for balancing redox equations that rarely fails:

1. Separate the equation into two half-reactions. One must contain an oxidation, and the other must include a reduction.

2. Balance each half-reaction separately.
   a. Balance the element oxidized or reduced.
   b. Balance any elements other than oxygen or hydrogen.
   c. Balance oxygen by adding water in the form of H_2O.

    d. In *acidic* solution, balance hydrogen by adding protons (H^+). In *basic* solution, balance hydrogen by adding water in the form H-OH, and then immediately add the same number of hydroxides (OH^-) to the other side of the equation.

    e. Balance the total charge on each side of the equation by adding electrons (e^-) to the side that is more positive.

3. Equalize the number of electrons lost and gained in the separate half-reactions by multiplying each by an integer. (You will remember this technique from math class as being similar to determining the LCM, or least common multiple.) For example, if the oxidation loses 2 electrons while the reduction gains 3 electrons, the least common multiple would be 6. Thus, you should multiply the oxidation by 3 and the reduction by 2 to acknowledge a transfer of 6 electrons.

4. Add the two half-reactions together. The electrons should cancel out from each side of the equation. You should be able to cancel other species as well. Protons, hydroxides, and waters frequently will cancel. Remember that H_2O and H-OH both mean water; they are written differently to balance oxygen and hydrogen, respectively.

5. Check to be sure that there is the same total charge on each side (though the total may be zero, it is not required to be zero—just the same). Then, check the total number of oxygen atoms on each side. If both the total charge and the number of oxygens balance, it is highly likely that you have balanced the overall reaction correctly.

Procedure Preview In this lab, iron(II) ammonium sulfate hexahydrate ("**FAS**," or "ferrous ammonium sulfate") will be titrated with a potassium permanganate solution to standardize it. Then a hydrogen peroxide/sulfuric acid solution will be titrated with the standardized $KMnO_4$ solution to analyze the hydrogen peroxide found in a commonly available consumer product. Finally, a solution of the iron supplement will be titrated with $KMnO_4$ solution to quantify the actual iron in the supplement and to compare it to the manufacturer's claim.

1. What is meant by "standardization"?

_____

_____

_____

_____

_____

2. Balance in *acid* solution:

$$Fe^{2+} + MnO_4^- \rightarrow Fe^{3+} + Mn^{2+}$$

_____

_____

_____

_____

_____

_____

3. "FAS" is a nickname for iron(II) ammonium sulfate hexahydrate. Why is it used as a standard in this experiment?

_____

_____

_____

_____

_____

_____

4. Balance this redox reaction: potassium permanganate, hydrogen peroxide, and sulfuric acid react to form manganese(II) sulfate, potassium sulfate, oxygen gas, and water.

_____

_____

_____

_____

_____

_____

5. In your lab notebook, draw data tables that list the measurements required for this lab. The tables will be filled in as the experiment is performed.

MATERIALS

- ~0.01 M KMnO$_4$
- 3% H$_2$O$_2$
- 6 M H$_2$SO$_4$
- "FAS" *ferrous ammonium sulfate*
- mortar and pestle

- micro-burets *(see Appendix B)*
- micro-stir bars *(see Appendix C)*
- 250-mL Erlenmeyer flask
- 50-mL buret *(see Appendix A)*
- 25-mL volumetric flask

PROCEDURE

I. Standardization of Potassium Permanganate Solution

Step A Measure out 0.2000 g FAS (your sample need not be exactly that amount, but you do need to know exactly how much you have).

Step B Dissolve the FAS sample in approximately 25 mL distilled water. If the sample does not dissolve readily, heat and stir the solution.

Step C Prepare a 50-mL buret for use with the KMnO$_4$ solution (refer to Appendix A, "Care and Feeding of the Buret"). After cleaning, be sure to rinse the buret with KMnO$_4$ solution. Fill the buret with KMnO$_4$ solution and run some through the tip of the buret. Note initial volume of the permanganate solution in the buret.

Step D Add 1 mL 6 M H$_2$SO$_4$ to the FAS solution.

Step E Titrate the FAS solution with KMnO$_4$ solution until a faint purple color persists for at least thirty seconds. Be sure to swirl or stir the solution continuously. Note the final volume of KMnO$_4$ solution in the buret.

Step F Repeat.

Calculations

1. Calculate the number of moles of FAS. ≈ 2 g   2 g
2. Calculate the number of moles of Fe^{2+}.
3. Calculate the number of moles of MnO$_4^-$.
4. Calculate the molarity of MnO$_4^-$.

Post-Lab Questions

1. Does FAS require special safety concerns? Obtain a Material Safety Data Sheet (MSDS) to verify.

_____

_____

_____

_____

2. Is potassium permanganate a safety problem? Obtain an MSDS to verify.

_____

_____

_____

_____

_____

II. Analysis of Hydrogen Peroxide by Redox Titration

Step A Refer to the previous standardization of the potassium permanganate solution.

Step B Using a micro-buret, measure 1.250 mL H_2O_2 solution into a 50-mL Erlenmeyer flask.

Step C Add 1 mL of 6 M H_2SO_4.

Step D Drop a micro-stir bar into the solution, set the flask onto a stirring/hot plate, and establish a gentle stirring rate. Add some distilled water if necessary to allow smooth mixing. Do not heat the solution.

Step E Using the same $KMnO_4$ buret as in the standardization analysis, titrate the hydrogen peroxide/sulfuric acid solution with $KMnO_4$ solution until a pale persistent purple exists. The characteristic color of the permanganate should last at least 30 seconds before fading.

Step F Repeat. If the result of the second trial is not within 5% of the first, repeat until a coherent result is reached.

Step G Mass a clean, dry 25-mL volumetric flask. Fill to the etched line with H_2O_2 solution and mass again.

Calculations

1. Calculate the density of the H_2O_2 solution.
2. Calculate the number of moles of $KMnO_4$ used in the titration.
3. Calculate the number of moles of H_2O_2 in the original sample.
4. Calculate the mass of H_2O_2 in the original sample.
5. Calculate the mass percent of H_2O_2 in the original sample.
6. Calculate the molarity of H_2O_2 in the original sample.

Post-Lab Questions

1. How does the calculated mass percent of hydrogen peroxide compare to the advertised mass percent?

_____

_____

_____

_____

_____

_____

2. What is the percent error?

_____

_____

_____

_____

_____

_____

3. Why is it that the calculated and advertised figures might be different?

_____

_____

_____

_____

_____

_____

_____

4. What are the measurement errors in this experiment and how significant are they?

_____

_____

_____

_____

_____

_____

_____

5. What other reasons might exist to explain any discrepancy between the experimental and advertised values?

_____

_____

_____

_____

_____

_____

_____

6. How is hydrogen peroxide used by consumers and in industry? Are there safety concerns? Obtain a Material Safety Data Sheet (MSDS) to verify any concerns.

_____

_____

_____

_____

_____

_____

_____

PROCEDURE
(continued)

III. Analysis of Iron Supplement by Redox Titration

Step A Mass the tablet or capsule of the iron supplement.

Step B If you have a tablet, crush it carefully with mortar and pestle. Put the crushed tablet in about 25 mL distilled water. Rinse mortar and pestle with distilled water to capture any residue. If it does not dissolve readily, heat and stir the solution. If using a gel capsule, carefully open the capsule and pour the contents into about 25 mL distilled water. Rinse any residue from the inside of the capsule. Heat and stir if necessary.

Step C Acidify the solution with 1 mL 6 M H_2SO_4.

Step D Titrate with $KMnO_4$ solution to a pale persistent purple. Be sure to note the initial and final volume from the buret.

Step E Repeat.

Calculations

1. Calculate the volume of $KMnO_4$ required.
2. Calculate the number of moles of MnO_4^- required.
3. Calculate the number of moles of Fe^{2+} required.
4. Calculate the number of grams of Fe^{2+}.
5. Calculate the mass percent of iron in the tablet or caplet.

Post-Lab Questions

1. Does the mass of iron that you calculated agree with the manufacturer's information as stated on the packaging? What is the percent error?

2. Suppose that the tablet contained a small quantity of another metal that could be oxidized by the permanganate solution. How would this affect the mass of iron that you calculate?

3. Suppose that the tablet included a nonreactive green coating. How might this affect the results of your titration?

4. Why did you add sulfuric acid before titrating?

Name _____   Date _____

Instructor _____   Section _____

Experiment

10

Determination of Acid Ionization Constant of a Weak Acid

PURPOSE

- Calculate the K_a of a weak monoprotic acid, given its pH and initial concentration
- Calculate the K_a of a weak monoprotic acid from pH of a solution of known amounts of acetic acid and sodium acetate
- Determine the K_a of a monoprotic or diprotic acid from a titration curve, using various analytic methods

INTRODUCTION

Weak acids are weak electrolytes, meaning that the molecular monoprotic acid acetic (ethanoic) acid, CH_3COOH, ionizes to a small extent in an aqueous solution, forming a proton (H^+) and CH_3COO^-, the conjugate base of CH_3COOH.

$$CH_3COOH_{(aq)} \leftrightarrow H^+_{(aq)} + CH_3COO^-_{(aq)} \qquad (1)$$

$$\text{Equilibrium constant } (K_a) = \frac{[H^+][CH_3COO^-]}{[CH_3COOH]}$$

As this is an equilibrium reaction, the relative strength of the acid may be thought of as the extent to which the acid ionizes, because the more an acid ionizes, the larger the **equilibrium constant**, or K_a, value.

Applying the Bronsted-Lowry definition of a base (as "a proton acceptor") makes determining the conjugate base easier. The **conjugate base** is the species that accepts the proton in the reverse reaction; that is,

$$H^+_{(aq)} + CH_3COO^-_{(aq)} \leftrightarrow CH_3COOH_{(aq)}$$

Another way to think of the conjugate base is as the species evolving from the acid after a proton has been donated (conjugate base = Acid − H^+). By either approach you choose, CH_3COO^- accepts a proton in the reverse reaction, so it is the conjugate base of CH_3COOH.

Some authorities show reaction (1) as a hydrolysis reaction with the acid donating a proton to water, forming the hydronium ion (H_3O^+) and the conjugate base of the acid. So the generic monoprotic acid hydrolysis reaction is

$$CH_3COOH_{(aq)} + H_2O_{(l)} \leftrightarrow H_3O^+_{(aq)} + CH_3COO^-_{(aq)} \qquad (2)$$

$$\text{Equilibrium constant } (K_a) = \frac{[H_3O^+][CH_3COO^-]}{[CH_3COOH]}$$

In this reaction, because it accepts a proton in the reverse reaction, CH_3COO^- is once again the conjugate base of CH_3COOH. You can think of the hydronium ion as a hydrated proton and the conjugate acid of water, which is the base in the forward reaction. These reactions really are interchangeable.

The expression for pH in reaction (1) is

$$pH = -\log[H^+]$$

The expression for pH for reaction (2) would not include the proton; rather, it must include the hydronium ion concentration instead:

$$pH = -\log[H_3O^+]$$

How does one determine the **ionization constant** (K_a) of an acid? By reviewing the equilibrium constant expression for acetic acid

$$K_a = \frac{[H^+][CH_3COO^-]}{[CH_3COOH]}$$

it is clear that one must determine the concentrations of H^+, CH_3COO^-, and CH_3COOH once equilibrium is established. Simply measuring the pH of an acetic acid solution, to verify that the pH is constant, is one way to conclude that equilibrium is established, because this shows that there is no net change in $[H^+]$.

Pre-Lab Preparation To gain a helpful mindset for understanding the necessary measurements for this lab, think how to go about calculating the solution to this problem:

> **What is the pH of 0.10 M acetic acid, given that the K_a of the acid is 1.8 $\times$ 10^{-5} at 298 K?**

Many sources use tables to show such calculations. As an example, the partial table below accounts for the initial concentrations in mol/L of the species (given as **I**), the change in concentrations needed to reach equilibrium (given as **C**), and finally, the equilibrium concentrations of all species (given as **E**).

$$K_a = \frac{[H^+][CH_3COO^-]}{[CH_3COOH]} = 1.8 \times 10^{-5}$$

		$CH_3COOH_{(aq)} \leftrightarrow$	$H^+_{(aq)}$	$+ CH_3COO^-_{(aq)}$
Initial concentration (M)	I	0.10	0	0
Change in concentration (M)	C			
Equilibrium concentration (M)	E			

This approach starts initially with the weak acid unionized, an assumption that dictates that the initial concentration of the products must be zero, because none of the acid has dissociated to form the products. To reach equilibrium, the acid must dissociate, so the change in its concentration must decrease, or be negative ($-$), while the change in concentrations of the products must increase, or be positive ($+$), as shown now in the **C** line of the table.

		CH₃COOH$_{(aq)}$ ↔	H⁺$_{(aq)}$	+ CH₃COO⁻$_{(aq)}$
Initial concentration *(M)*	I	0.10	0	0
Change in concentration *(M)*	C	−	+	+
Equilibrium concentration *(M)*	E			

The reaction stoichiometry must be used to determine the magnitude of the change. In the case of acetic acid, the mole ratio of acetic acid to proton to acetate is 1 : 1 : 1. This gives only the relative change in concentration, but we can define the variable x as "the change in concentration of acetic acid." Then, using the 1 : 1 : 1 stoichiometric mole ratio, we can rewrite the **C** line in the table, as follows:

		CH₃COOH$_{(aq)}$ ↔	H⁺$_{(aq)}$	+ CH₃COO⁻$_{(aq)}$
Initial concentration *(M)*	I	0.10	0	0
Change in concentration *(M)*	C	−x	+x	+x
Equilibrium concentration *(M)*	E			

Because E = I + C, you can determine the equilibrium concentration by simply adding the **I** line to the **C** line:

		CH₃COOH$_{(aq)}$ ↔	H⁺$_{(aq)}$	+ CH₃COO⁻$_{(aq)}$
Initial concentration *(M)*	I	0.10	0	0
Change in concentration *(M)*	C	−x	+x	+x
Equilibrium concentration *(M)*	E	0.10 − x	+x	+x

Substituting the **E** line into the equilibrium constant expression yields the following:

$$1.8 \times 10^{-5} = \frac{[x][x]}{[0.10 - x]}$$

At this point, there is a "fork in the road." Because the magnitude of the K_a is very small compared to the magnitude of the initial concentration of the acetic acid—more than 5,000 times smaller—we recognize that the amount of acetic acid x that ionizes will likely be much smaller than the initial concentration. So when x is subtracted from 0.10, it is unlikely that the value of 0.10 will change, once the difference is represented to the correct number of significant figures. So, it is reasonable to *assume* that $x \ll 0.10$. Doing so allows us to simplify the expression 0.10 − x to 0.10. Then the equilibrium equation becomes

$$1.8 \times 10^{-5} = \frac{[x][x]}{[0.10]}$$

which can be solved for x, without using the quadratic formula, to give 0.0013 *M*. Substituting this x value back into the table, we have

		CH₃COOH$_{(aq)}$ ↔	H⁺$_{(aq)}$	+ CH₃COO⁻$_{(aq)}$
Initial concentration *(M)*	I	0.10	0	0
Change in concentration *(M)*	C	−0.0013	+0.0013	+0.0013
Equilibrium concentration *(M)*	E	0.10 − 0.0013	0.0013	0.0013

As we assumed, the expression $0.10 - 0.0013$ is equivalent to 0.10, once the rules of significant figures are applied. Although $0.10 - 0.0013 = 0.0987$, the rules for significant figures dictate that the difference be reported to 2 decimal places. Thus 0.0987 must be rounded to 0.10, and the assumption that $x \ll 0.10$, *so that* $0.10 - x = 0.10$, is shown to be valid. This assumption can also be checked by solving the original quadratic equation for the equilibrium constant:

$$1.8 \times 10^{-5} = \frac{[x][x]}{[0.10 - x]}$$

There are a number of ways to solve for the constant. First, many modern calculators have SOLVER functions that can be used to solve this quadratic. Alternatively, one can resort to the old standby, pencil-on-paper method of the quadratic formula:

$$x = \frac{-b \pm \sqrt{b^2 - 4ac}}{2a}$$

To solve for x, we rearrange our quadratic to

$$0 = x^2 + 1.8 \times 10^{-5}x - 1.8 \times 10^{-6}$$

and substitute into the formula the coefficients:

$$a = 1 \qquad b = 1.8 \times 10^{-5} \qquad c = -1.8 \times 10^{-6}$$

Bear in mind that although there are two roots to any quadratic, only one is a possible answer for this problem. If the root is negative, it can easily be ruled out because negative x is not possible in an equilibrium problem. (*Note*: the "$-$" in "$-x$" that appears in the ICE table indicates a decrease in concentration, not a negative value for x.) Also, because x represents the equilibrium concentration of H^+ and CH_3COO^-, it cannot be a negative number. Moreover, if a root of the quadratic equation were substituted back into the table and the subtraction yielded a negative concentration at equilibrium, this would be an impossible situation.

And finally, the roots of the quadratic can also be found by graphing the quadratic equation. Here are instructions for using a generic Texas Instruments graphing calculator:

1. Turn on your calculator by pressing the "ON" button in the bottom left corner.
2. Press the "Y=" button in the upper left-hand corner.
3. Set the equation equal to zero.
   i. You must subtract 1.8E−5 from both sides of the equation so that it reads $0 = \{(x) (x) / (0.10 - x)\} - 1.8E-5$.
   ii. You can then plug this equation into your calculator.
4. Then in "Y2," set the equation equal to zero.
5. Press the ZOOM button, the middle button on the top line, and scroll down to "6:ZStandard" and press ENTER.
6. Next press the TRACE button, the second-to-last button in the top right of the calculator.
7. Now press the "2nd" button, below the "Y=" button, and then press the CALC button (this button is the same as the GRAPH button, but now uses its second function).
8. Scroll down to "5:Intersect" and press ENTER.

9. The graph screen will come up again with the equation and the questions "First curve?" Press ENTER twice (you are selecting both graphs) and then you must scroll with the arrow keys right or left to make a guess at where your graph crosses the x-axis. Then press ENTER.

10. In the bottom left corner of the screen you will see "X= __." This is one of your x values.

11. To find the other x value, repeat Steps 7–9, but this time use the other intersection point.

12. You now have two values for x that can satisfy the equation. However, only one of these numbers is a plausible answer (the value should be positive and a relatively small number, close to 0.0013).

At this point, the pH of the solution can be calculated. Because, at equilibrium, $[H^+] = 0.0013$ M, then

$$pH = -\log[0.0013] = 2.88$$

According to rules for significant figure for pH values (or pANYTHING values), the numbers to the right of the decimal point are significant. Because the pH will have two decimal places, 2.88 is the correct pH value.

Procedure Preview In our analysis of the problem to this point, the K_a and initial concentration of the acid were used to determine the pH of the solution. Now suppose the problem were reframed; for example:

> **How can you calculate the K_a of a weak monoprotic acid given that the pH of a 0.10 M solution is 2.88?**

Could the problem be worked backwards? Certainly, and you are now in a position to begin your lab experimentation with equilibrium reactions of weak acids. Speak with your instructor about which of the three methods presented in the following pages you are to carry out.

Method I: Determining K_a of a Weak Acid by Using pH and Concentration of Acid

To determine the K_a of an acid, all one needs is the pH of the solution and the concentration of the acid. Measuring the pH requires a calibrated pH probe. By reviewing Experiment 8 of this lab manual, in which the mass percent of acetic acid in vinegar was found, you will recall that the concentration of an acid can be determined by titrating a known volume of acid solution, using a standardized base and phenolphthalein as the indicator. Then, looking at the calculation tables, the pH can be used to calculate the equilibrium concentration of H^+ and acetate ion. The titration data can be used to calculate the initial concentration y of acetic acid.

		$CH_3COOH_{(aq)} \leftrightarrow$	$H^+_{(aq)}$	$+ CH_3COO^-_{(aq)}$
Initial concentration (M)	I	y	0	0
Change in concentration (M)	C	$-x$	$+x$	$+x$
Equilibrium concentration (M)	E	$y - x$	$+x$	$+x$

Now, all that separates the K_a value from you is the substitution of your values into the equilibrium constant expression and making the calculations.

Copyright © Peoples Publishing Group. Photocopying not permitted.

MATERIALS

➤ ethanoic (acetic) acid solution
➤ standardized NaOH solution
➤ phenolphthalein
➤ buret
➤ measuring device for 10.00 mL (pipet, buret, or graduated cylinder)

➤ calibrated pH probe
➤ beaker
➤ microstir bar *(see Appendix C)*
➤ magnetic stir plate
➤ distilled water (in squirt bottle)

PROCEDURE

In this procedure you will find the concentration of ions in solution to determine K_a given initial pH.

Step A Prepare the buret by rinsing it with standardized NaOH; remove any air bubbles from tip of buret.

Step B Record initial volume of NaOH in your data table.

Step C Record actual concentration of NaOH solution in your data table.

Step D Measure pH of acetic acid sample.

Step E Transfer 10.00 mL of the acetic acid sample to a beaker, using a measuring device determined by your instructor. Record the exact volume of acid that you added.

Step F Add 2 drops of phenolphthalein to solution and a microstir bar to beaker.

Step G Place beaker on the magnetic stir plate.

Step H Titrate the acid sample by adding NaOH solution until a faint pink color is permanent. You must be patient close to the endpoint, because it takes a few seconds for complete mixing of the solution and the color change of indicator.

Step I Record the final volume of NaOH.

Step J Repeat Steps A–I, if directed by your instructor.

Calculations (Method I)

1. Calculate the number of moles of NaOH that were needed to neutralize the acetic acid sample.
2. Using the volume of acid you titrated, calculate the concentration of the acetic acid sample.
3. Using the pH of the acetic acid sample, calculate the equilibrium concentration of H^+.
4. Using your answer to Question 3, calculate the equilibrium concentrations of the acetate ion and acetic acid.
5. Using your answers to Questions 3 and 4, calculate the K_a for acetic acid.
6. Repeat for a second sample, if applicable.
7. Compare your calculated K_a with the actual K_a of acetic acid.
8. Propose one possible error that could have resulted in a calculated K_a that is too great. Explain how this error would have resulted.

Method II: Determining K_a from pH of Solution Made from Known Amounts of Acid and Conjugate Base

This method will take advantage of an important fact of acid equilibrium highlighted by the following problem:

How can you calculate the pH of a solution made when 25.0 mL of 0.10 M acetic acid is mixed with 50.0 mL of 0.050 M sodium acetate? (K_a acetic acid = 1.8×10^{-5}. Assume volumes are additive.)

First, it is important to address the solution of sodium acetate to determine that

➤ it is a strong electrolyte, so the sodium acetate ionizes 100%;
➤ the acetate ion is the conjugate base of acetic acid.

Thus, when these two solutions are mixed, there is no chemical reaction, but rather a solution containing a weak acid and the salt of its conjugate base. The resulting solution can still be described by the following equilibrium:

$$CH_3COOH_{(aq)} \leftrightarrow H^+_{(aq)} + CH_3COO^-_{(aq)}$$

In order to address this equilibrium, we must determine the initial concentrations of all species after the two solutions are mixed.

$$[CH_3COOH]_{initial} = \frac{0.10 \text{ moles } CH_3COOH}{1.00 \text{ L}} \left| \frac{25.0 \text{ mL}}{(25.0 \text{ mL} + 50.0 \text{ mL})} \right. = 0.033 \, M$$

$$[CH_3COO^-]_{initial} = \frac{0.050 \text{ moles } NaCH_3COO}{1.00 \text{ L}} \left| \frac{50.0 \text{ mL}}{(50.0 \text{ mL} + 25.0 \text{ mL})} \right. = 0.033 \, M$$

Now, back to the equilibrium. It is vital to note that *initially* both the acid and its conjugate base are present:

		$CH_3COOH_{(aq)} \leftrightarrow$	$H^+_{(aq)}$	$+ CH_3COO^-_{(aq)}$
Initial concentration (*M*)	I	0.33	0	0.33
Change in concentration (*M*)	C	$-x$	$+x$	$+x$
Equilibrium concentration (*M*)	E	$0.33 - x$	$+x$	$0.33 + x$

Because the acid has not ionized initially, no protons are present and, therefore, some must be formed as the reaction shifts to achieve equilibrium.

$$1.8 \times 10^{-5} = \frac{[x][0.33 + x]}{[0.33 - x]}$$

Because the conjugate is present to start, less of the acid has to ionize to get the reaction quotient, Q, to equal K and achieve equilibrium. So based on the ideas discussed earlier in the introductory problem, let us *assume $x \ll 0.33$*, so that the addition of x to 0.33 or the subtraction of x from 0.33 will not, to significant figures, alter this value; in other words, $0.33 - x = 0.33$ and also $0.33 + x = 0.33$. (As before, check that your assumptions are valid. To significant figures:

$$0.33 + 0.000018 = 0.33 \text{ and } 0.33 - 0.000018 = 0.33$$

It is left as an exercise for you to conduct a second check, by solving the quadratic equation by some method, to confirm the validity of the assumptions.)
Now the equilibrium is simplified to:

$$1.8 \times 10^{-5} = \frac{[x][0.33]}{[0.33]}$$

and, because 0.33 divided by itself is 1,

$$1.8 \times 10^{-5} = x = [H^+] \text{ and}$$

$$pH = -\log[1.8 \times 10^{-5}] = 4.74$$

Moreover, because

$$K_a = \frac{[H^+][CH_3COO^-]}{[CH_3COOH]}$$

when $[CH_3COOH] = [CH_3COO^-]$

$$K_a = \frac{[H^+][\cancel{CH_3COO^-}]}{[\cancel{CH_3COOH}]} = [H^+]$$

Take note of this very special relationship: when the equilibrium concentration of an acid equals the concentration of its conjugate base,

$$[H^+] = K_a \text{ and } -\log[H^+] = -\log K_a$$
$$\text{so, } pH = pK_a$$

When the equilibrium relationship is rearranged as follows

$$K_a = \frac{[H^+][CH_3COO^-]}{[CH_3COOH]} \quad \text{or} \quad \frac{K_a}{[H^+]} = \frac{[CH_3COO^-]}{[CH_3COOH]}$$

and the $-\log$ of the two sides are taken, then

$$pK_a - pH = -\log\left\{\frac{[CH_3COO^-]}{[CH_3COOH]}\right\}$$

which can be restated algebraically as

$$pH = pK_a + \log\left\{\frac{[CH_3COO^-]}{[CH_3COOH]}\right\}$$

which is the **Henderson-Hasselbalch equation**.

In brief, by making a solution that has equal concentrations (therefore, equal moles) of acid and conjugate base, and taking the pH of this solution, the pK_a of the acid will also be measured. Then the K_a can be calculated using

$$10^{-pK_a} = K_a$$

It is important to note that, because K_a is constant at a given temperature, it is the ratio of concentrations of conjugate base to weak acid that determines the $[H^+]$ and, as a result, the pH.

MATERIALS

- ➤ acetic acid solution
- ➤ standardized NaOH solution
- ➤ phenolphthalein
- ➤ buret
- ➤ measuring device for 25.00 mL (pipet, buret, or graduated cylinder)

- ➤ calibrated pH probe
- ➤ beaker
- ➤ microstir bar *(see Appendix C)*
- ➤ magnetic stir plate
- ➤ distilled water (in squirt bottle)

PROCEDURE

In this procedure you will first determine the concentrations of acetic acid and sodium acetate in solution in order to calculate K_a.

Step A Prepare the buret by rinsing it with standardized NaOH; remove any air bubbles from the tip.

Step B Record the initial volume of NaOH in your data table.

Step C Record the actual concentration of NaOH solution.

PROCEDURE
(continued)

Step D Transfer 25.00 mL of acetic acid sample to a beaker, using a measuring device chosen by your instructor. Record the exact volume of acid added.

Step E Add 2 drops of phenolphthalein to solution and the microstir bar to beaker.

Step F Place the beaker on the magnetic stir plate.

Step G Titrate the acid sample by adding NaOH solution until faint pink color is permanent. Be patient close to the endpoint, because it takes a few seconds for complete mixing of the solution and color change of indicator.

Step H Record the final volume of NaOH.

Step I Label beaker with this sample and keep sample.

Step J Measure a second sample of acetic acid that is exactly the same volume as the sample you titrated. See Step D for the exact volume used in first sample.

Step K Pour this sample, measured in Step J, into the beaker containing the titrated sample of acetic saved in Step I. Stir thoroughly.

Step L Rinse the pH meter tip with distilled water and pat dry with paper towel.

Step M Place cleaned pH probe in sample and allow pH reading to stabilize while solution is being stirred (manually or by using stir bar and magnetic stirrer). Record the pH of this solution.

Step N Dilute this sample by adding 10.0 mL of distilled water and mix thoroughly.

Step O Rinse the pH meter tip with distilled water and pat dry with paper towel.

Step P Place the cleaned pH probe in the sample and allow pH reading to stabilize while the solution is being stirred (manually or with stir bar and magnetic stirrer). Record the pH of this solution.

Calculations (Method II)

1. Write a balanced chemical reaction equation for the titration reaction between acetic acid and sodium hydroxide.
2. Calculate the number of moles of NaOH needed to neutralize the acetic acid sample.
3. Calculate the number of moles of acetic acid in your sample.
4. Calculate the moles of sodium acetate that were formed during the titration.
5. Compare the number of moles of acetic acid and sodium acetate present in the solution you made during Step K.
6. Assuming that volumes are additive, calculate the concentrations of acetic acid and sodium acetate in the solution made during Step K.
7. Using the pH from Step M and the answer to Question 6, calculate K_a for acetic acid.
8. Compare your calculated K_a with the actual K_a of acetic acid.
9. Compare the pH reading taken in Step M with that taken in Step P.
10. Did you expect the pH to change much when the sample was diluted? Explain why or why not. Be sure to show quantitative calculations to support your answer.

Post-Lab Questions

Did you need to know:

1. Exact volume of acid or base? Explain.

_____

_____

_____

_____

_____

2. Initial concentration of the base? Explain.

_____

_____

_____

_____

_____

_____

3. Initial pH of the acid or base? Explain.

_____

_____

_____

_____

_____

_____

4. Final pH of the acid after the titration? Explain.

_____

_____

_____

_____

_____

5. Final pH of the mixture from Step K? Explain.

_____

_____

_____

_____

_____

Method III: Determining K_a of a Weak Acid from a Titration Curve

The previous two methods work very well and quickly to determine the K_a of a weak monoprotic acid. But there is another method for determining the K_a of an acid, and this one also provides additional valuable information—such as how protic the acid is, and what indicator(s) will work to show the endpoint of a titration. This third method involves a titration, but in this case the pH of the resulting solution is recorded after each addition of a known volume of base. A graph of the pH on the y-axis, versus the total volume of base added on the x-axis, is called a **titration** curve. The shape of the curve tells whether the acid is strong or weak, as illustrated in Figure 10.1.

Figure 10.1

Titration Curves of Strong and Weak Acids

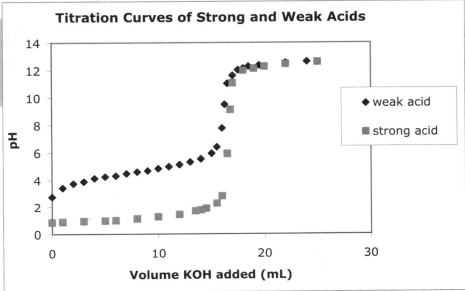

If there is an initial rise in pH, after addition of a small amount of base, which levels off over a wide region before transitioning from an acidic pH to a basic pH, then the acid is a weak acid. A strong acid titration curve does not have this initial bump; rather, there is a gradual increase in pH before the transition to basic pH. Notice that these transitions occur when the pH changes extremely fast upon addition of an extremely small volume of base. It is for this reason that you add the base by the drop as you approach the endpoint of a titration using an indicator: because a few drops of base cause an extreme change in pH, the indicator will change color upon addition of one drop of base.

In addition, the shape of a titration curve tells whether the acid is mono-, di-, or triprotic. As Figures 10.2 and 10.3 show, if the titration curve contains one hump, the acid is monoprotic; if there are two humps on the curve, the acid is diprotic. A triprotic acid would have three humps.

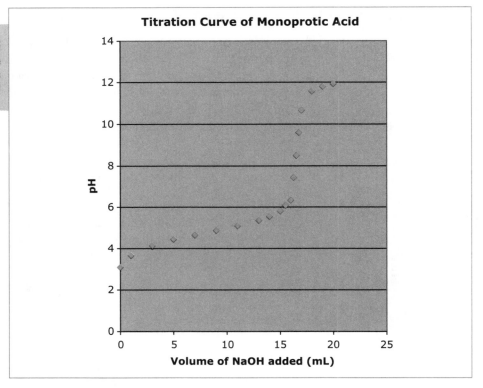

Figure 10.2
Titration Curve of Monoprotic Acid

Titration Curve of Monoprotic Acid

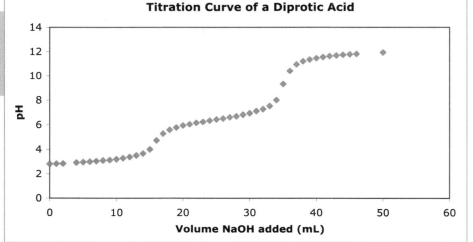

Figure 10.3
Titration Curve of a Diprotic Acid

Titration Curve of a Diprotic Acid

It is likely that other acid-base titrations you have performed used an indicator to show the endpoint of the titration. It is the endpoint of the titration when the indicator undergoes a specific color change. It turns out that indicators change colors at specific pH values (see Experiment 11, on determining K_{in} of bromocresol green, for more information on how an indicator works), so when enough base has been added, the pH of the resulting solution will become more basic. When a certain pH is reached, the indicator will change color and the experimenter is trained to stop adding base at this point. We assume that this is the point where the acid has been completely neutralized by addition of the stoichiometric amount of base.

It turns out, however, that the endpoint may not be the true stoichiometric end of the reaction, but rather indicate the pH at which the indicator itself loses a proton, resulting in a color change. Did you ever wonder how one determines which indicator to use to do this? A titration curve can tell you. The true stoichiometric equivalence point can be determined by careful analysis of the titration curve, looking for the region on the curve where the concavity of the curve changes. The titration curve, then, shows the **equivalence point**, not the endpoint. At the equivalence point, all of the acid has reacted and converted into the conjugate base of the acid. The pH at the equivalence can be used to determine the indicator(s) that change colors a little past the pH at the equivalence point. *Note:* if it takes 25.00 mL of NaOH to reach the equivalence point during the titration of a weak monoprotic acid, it will take 12.50 mL to reach the 1/2-equivalence point, and this is a very important point on the titration, because at this point the concentration of the weak acid will equal the concentration of its conjugatge base (because 1/2 of the acid has been neutralized). So, as demonstrated in Method II, when

$$[HA] = [A^-], \text{ then } K_a = [H^+]$$

and the pH equals the pK_a of the acid.

The pH of the solution changes very gradually around the 1/2-equivalence point when the base is added and the ratio of concentrations of [conjugate base]/[acid] is close to 1. This is called the buffer region of the titration curve, because this is where there is a mixture of the weak acid and its conjugate base in a ratio between 0.1 and 10.

Clearly, the most important point to determine on a titration curve is the equivalence point, since from this the 1/2-equivalence point and K_a are calculated. If the acid is diprotic, there are two equivalence points, and the second equivalence point will show the more dramatic pH change and is easier to find and analyze. But, 1/2 the volume to the second is not a 1/2-equivalence point; rather, it is the first equivalence point. So, 1/4 the volume to the second equivalence point will give the volume of the first 1/2-equivalence point:

$$K_{a1} = \frac{[H^+][HA^-]}{[H_2A]}$$

The pH here equals pK_{a1}. The second 1/2-equivalence point is halfway between the first and second equivalence point, or 3/4 of the volume of the second equivalence point. The pH here will equal pK_{a2}. Also, the pH at the final equivalence point will tell you what indicator(s) will indicate the endpoint of the titration. It should go without saying, since the equivalence point tells you the volume of base added to neutralize the acid, and the shape of the titration curve tells you the reaction stoichiometry of the acid and base, that the titration curve allows for the most thorough analysis of an acid.

The equivalence point can be determined by following either the "circle method," "line method," or "right angle method." Equivalence point can also be found by taking the first or second derivative of the titration curve data. There now follow step-by-step approaches to determining the equivalence point using each of these methods. When studying the circle, line, or right-angle methods, refer to a copy of Figure 10.4, which it will be helpful for you to sketch in as you study the steps.

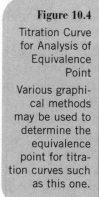

Figure 10.4

Titration Curve for Analysis of Equivalence Point

Various graphical methods may be used to determine the equivalence point for titration curves such as this one.

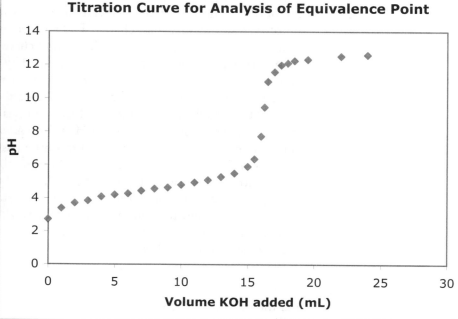

Circle Method to Determine Equivalence Point(s) on Titration Curve

1. Graph the titration curve to determine whether it is of a mono- or diprotic acid. Find the transition area that occurs with the largest volume of base added. This area will have the steepest positive slope, where the pH change is greatest in respect to the least change in volume. This area will have the only (or second) equivalence point.

2. Fit two curved regions that bracket the transition from low to high pH, using circles that fit the natural curvature in each region. (Either a rubber stopper—with one hole if possible—or a beaker provide nice circle templates to use in this step. Find the correct-sized template by trying a variety of different-sized circles, then trace the one on the titration curve that touches the most data points.)

3. Find the center of each circle drawn in Step 2 and mark each center. (The center of a circle that was traced using a one-holed rubber stopper *is* the hole.)

4. Draw a line connecting the centers of these circles

5. The point where the line connecting the centers intersects the titration curve is the equivalence point.

6. Drop a perpendicular from this intersection point to the *x*-axis to determine the volume of base added to reach the equivalence point.

7. Calculate 1/2 this volume of base. This volume represents the 1/2-equivalence point if the acid analyzed is a monoprotic acid; or, if the acid is a diprotic acid, the volume at the first equivalence point.

Line Method to Determine Equivalence Point(s) on Titration Curve

1. Using a straightedge, draw a line of best fit for the first region on the titration curve where the pH is most stable.

2. Repeat Step 1, but do this for the region at the end of the titration curve.

3. Draw a best-fit line for the steep region on the titration curve where the pH change is greatest for the least change in volume.

4. Mark the two points where this steep line from Step 3 intersects each of the lines drawn in Steps 1 and 2.

5. Measure the distance between the two points marked in Step 4. Calculate the midpoint between these points and mark this point clearly.

6. Drop a perpendicular from this midpoint mark to the x-axis to determine the volume of base added to reach the equivalence point.

7. Calculate half this volume of base. This volume represents the half-equivalence point if the acid analyzed is a monoprotic acid, or, if the acid is a diprotic acid, the volume at the first equivalence point.

Right-Angle Method to Determine Equivalence Point(s) on Titration Curve

1. Taking a T-square or other device with a true right angle, slide it along the x-axis until the curve goes vertical. This region indicates the equivalence point because it is the steepest part of the curve.

2. Calculate half of the so-indicated volume of base. This volume represents the half-equivalence point, if the acid analyzed is a monoprotic acid. If the acid is a diprotic acid, the volume represents the first equivalence point.

Derivative Method to Determine Equivalence Point(s) on Titration Curve

Although some programs for the computer and calculator will calculate the first- and second-derivatives for you, finding derivatives can be done by hand or on a spreadsheet using the raw pH and volume data. The first derivative is the

$$\frac{\text{change in pH}}{\text{change in volume}} \quad \text{or} \quad \frac{\Delta pH}{\Delta V}$$

that is, the slope of the line tangent to a given data point. To calculate this value, you must perform a series of identical calculations using sliding pairs of the volume and pH data. Because each calculation creates a new data point by using a pair of data points from the original pH and volume data, each derivative results in one fewer data points—that is, one data point lost per derivative taken. The data in Table 10.1 are taken from the titration of acetic acid; it is the pH and volume of NaOH added for the region near the equivalence point that are given.

Following the table is a description of how to calculate the first derivative by hand. For clarity, only the data from the titration curve for acetic acid that brackets the equivalence point, not all the data points, are analyzed. However, first derivatives along the entire titration curve could be calculated using the method that is laid out. Note that the solutions to the equations set up in Columns 4 and 5 are shown in **bold**.

	Column 1	Column 2	Column 3	Column 4	Column 5
Table 10.1 Data from Titration Curve and Calculation of First Derivative	Sample #	Volume of NaOH (in mL)	pH	Average Volume (in mL)	$\dfrac{\Delta pH}{\Delta Volume}$ (First Derivative)
	S1	11.00	5.11		
	S2	13.00	5.37	(S2 + S1)/2 (13.00 + 11.00)/2 **12.00**	$(pH_2 - pH_1)/(V_2 - V_1)$ (5.37 − 5.11)/(13.00 − 11.00) **0.13**
	S3	14.00	5.56	(S3 + S2)/2 (14.00 + 13.00)/2 **13.50**	$(pH_3 - pH_2)/(V_3 - V_2)$ (5.56 − 5.37)/(14.00 − 13.00) **0.19**
	S4	15.00	5.82	(S4 + S3)/2 (15.00 + 14.00)/2 **14.50**	$(pH_4 - pH_3)/(V_4 - V_3)$ (5.82 − 5.56)/(15.00 − 14.00) **0.26**
	S5	15.50	6.10	(S5 + S4)/2 (15.50 + 15.00)/2 **15.25**	$(pH_5 - pH_4)/(V_5 - V_4)$ (6.10 − 5.82)/(15.50 − 15.00) **0.56**
	S6	16.00	6.35	(S6 + S5)/2 (16.00 + 15.50)/2 **15.75**	$(pH_6 - pH_5)/(V_6 - V_5)$ (6.35 − 6.10)/(16.00 − 15.50) **0.50**
	S7	16.25	7.44	(S7 + S6)/2 (16.25 + 16.00)/2 **16.13**	$(pH_7 - pH_6)/(V_7 - V_6)$ (7.44 − 6.35)/(16.25 − 16.00) **4.36**
	S8	16.50	8.50	(S8 + S7)/2 (16.50 + 16.25)/2 **16.38**	$(pH_8 - pH_7)/(V_8 - V_7)$ (8.50 − 7.44)/(16.50 − 16.25) **4.24**
	S9	16.75	9.60	(S9 + S8)/2 (16.75 + 16.50)/2 **16.63**	$(pH_9 - pH_8)/(V_9 - V_8)$ (9.60 − 8.50)/(16.75 − 16.50) **4.40**
	S10	17.00	10.68	(S10 + S9)/2 (17.00 + 16.75)/2 **16.88**	$(pH_{10} - pH_9)/(V_{10} - V_9)$ (10.68 − 9.60)/(17.00 − 16.75) **4.32**
	S11	18.00	11.58	(S11 + S10)/2 (18.00 + 17.00)/2 **17.50**	$(pH_{11} - pH_{10})/(V_{11} - V_{10})$ (11.58 − 10.68)/(18.00 − 17.00) **0.90**
	S12	19.00	11.80	(S12 + S11)/2 (19.00 + 18.00)/2 **18.50**	$(pH_{12} - pH_{11})/(V_{12} - V_{11})$ (11.80 − 11.58)/(19.00 − 18.00) **0.22**

The data are analyzed in pairs, with the average of the volumes taken first, using sequential sliding pairs of volumes, as shown in Column 4. Then the first derivative (ΔpH / ΔVolume) is calculated, also using sequential sliding pairs, as shown in Column 5. Now the first derivative of the titration curve graph may be graphed, as shown in Figure 10.5, where the first derivative data from Column 5 are plotted on the y-axis versus the average volume data on the x-axis.

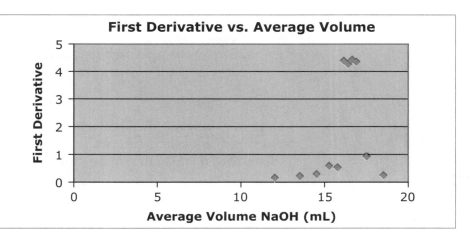

Figure 10.5
First Derivative vs. Average Volume

The volume at the equivalence point is determined from this graph by dropping a perpendicular to the x-axis from the maximum y value, as this is the point where the slope changes from positive to negative, a characteristic of the point where the concavity of the titration curve changes.

The second derivative can then be calculated by the same process as for the first derivative, using sliding sequential pairs. But instead of analyzing the pH and volume data, the data of average volume (Column 4) and the first derivative data (Column 5) are used. Again, you will end up with one fewer data point.

The reaction between a weak acid and a strong base may be modeled as a three-step process:

Step 1 **Reaction between the hydrated proton and hydroxide ion**

$$H^+_{(aq)} + OH^-_{(aq)} \rightarrow H_2O_{(l)}$$

The number of moles of proton that react with the base is determined by the limiting reactant.

Step 2 **Replacement of reacted hydrated proton by ionization of more weak acid**
As the concentration of hydrated proton decreases when it reacts with the hydroxide ion, more of the unionized weak acid, HA, ionizes to replace the reacted $H^+_{(aq)}$. This can be thought of as an application of Le Chatelier's Principle.

$$HA_{(aq)} \leftrightarrow H^+_{(aq)} + A^-_{(aq)}$$

Step 3 **Reestablishment of equilibrium between weak acid and its conjugate base**

$$HA_{(aq)} \leftrightarrow H^+_{(aq)} + A^-_{(aq)}$$

As more base is added, Steps 1 and 2 continue until all the added hydroxide ion, which is the limiting reactant, reacts, leaving only HA and A^- in solution. But, as soon as all the base has reacted, the equilibrium between HA and A^- is reestablished by further ionization of the weak acid. Because some of the conjugate base is already present, less of the HA will ionize, so less free H^+ is in solution at equilibrium, resulting in a higher (more basic) pH. Because the K_a has not changed, the extent of the ionization of HA is dictated by the ratio of concentrations of conjugate base to unionized acid, $[A^-]/[HA]$, because

$$\frac{K_a}{[H^+]} = \frac{[A^-]}{[HA]}$$

This explains why the pH of the solution becomes more basic throughout the titration even as there is unreacted acid in solution.

Remember, there are three important points on a titration curve:

> ➤ *The point when no base has been added.* The pH at this point represents the pH of a weak acid solution.

> ➤ *The half-equivalence point.* For a monoprotic acid, this point is the pH when half of the acid has been neutralized.

> ➤ *The equivalence point.* This is the point where the stoichiometric amount of base has been added to react with all ionizable protons in the acid.

MATERIALS

➤ pH meter
➤ standardized NaOH solution
➤ acetic acid solution
➤ 100-mL beaker
➤ 50-mL buret
➤ pipet bulb
➤ pH standards
   (pH=4.00 and pH=10.00)

➤ ring stand
➤ microstir bar (*see Appendix C*)
➤ magnetic stirrer
➤ volumetric pipet
   (25-mL or combination of others)
➤ buret clamp
➤ clamp
➤ distilled water (in squirt bottle)

PROCEDURE

In this section of the lab you will titrate a variety of weak acids with a standardized solution of a strong base. You will collect the titration data of solution pH as a function of volume of strong base added, and this curve will then be analyzed to determine the concentration of the weak acid and its ionization constant(s), K_a(s), which will be compared to the literature value(s).

Step A Calibrate the pH meter. Your instructor will give you specific instructions.

Step B Rinse the pH meter tip with distilled water and pat dry with a paper towel.

Step C Prepare the buret by rinsing it with NaOH solution and removing any air bubbles from the tip.

Step D Fill the buret to 0.00 mL mark.

Step E Measure 15.00 mL of acetic acid solution, using a volumetric pipet, then place in a 100-mL beaker along with a microstir bar.

Step F Place the pH meter in solution and wait for the pH reading to be constant.

Step G Record the pH when 0.00 mL NaOH is added.

Step H Add 1–2 mL of NaOH and allow the solutions to mix thouroughly for one minute.

Step I Record pH when the reading has stabilized, and enter the exact volume of base added (to 0.01 mL).

Step J Repeat steps H and I. *Be sure to record total volume of base added, not the amount of NaOH added after last recorded volume.*

Copyright © Peoples Publishing Group. Photocopying not permitted.

PROCEDURE
(continued)

Step K Repeat until _____ mL of base has been added. *Add smaller, incremental volumes of NaOH as the pH reading approaches 6.0.* Continue to do so until change in pH decreases per volume of NaOH added.

Step L Finally, the pH of the resulting solution will not change appreciably after more base is added. At this point, the pH reading will be very constant for four consecutive volumes of base added. Stop. You have completed the titration.

Calculations (Method III)

You are now ready to analyze your titration curves. Your instructor will tell you which method(s) to use in the analysis.

1. How many ionizable protons does your acid contain?
2. Determine the equivalence point(s) following these methods:
   a. Use circles to determine the *change in concavity* of the transition region of the titration curve. The point when the concavity changes is the equivalence point.
   b. Draw a best-fit line by hand using as many points as possible on the titration curves in the regions where there is not much change in pH (these lines are roughly horizontal). Exactly how many points these lines include depends on the number of data points in these regions. However, by moving a straightedge on these regions, you will find the lines that contain the greatest number of your data points. Then draw a line through as many points as possible in the transition region where the rate of change in pH is extremely great. Find the midpoint of this vertical line (where the pH changes rapidly) between the two points where it intersects the horizontal lines (where the pH changes slowly). Drop a perpendicular to the x-axis from the midpoint. This will give you the volume needed to reach this equivalence point.
   c. Use the right angle method: taking a T-square or something else with a true right angle, slide it along the x-axis until the curve goes vertical. This will be the equivalence point since it is the steepest part of the curve.
   d. Take the first and second derivatives of the titration curve data using a calculator or computer. Graph the first derivative data and the second derivative data. The peak(s) of the first derivative data, where the slope changes from positive to negative, is (are) equivalence point(s). The equivalence point(s) on the second derivative graph is (are) where the graph crosses the x-axis.
3. Use the equivalence point to determine the K_a of the acid.
4. Which acid/base indicator would you choose to show the endpoint of the titration of each acid? Explain your choice thoroughly.

Post-Lab Questions

Predict how the calculated concentration of an acid would be affected—too high, too low, or not affected—by the following laboratory procedures. *Thoroughly explain* your answers.

1. The buret, after rinsing with distilled water, is filled with standardized hydroxide solution; the acid solution is immediately titrated to the endpoint.

   _____

   _____

   _____

   _____

   _____

   _____

   _____

   _____

   _____

   _____

   _____

   _____

   _____

   _____

2. An air bubble passes unnoticed through the tip of the buret during the titration.

   _____

   _____

   _____

   _____

   _____

   _____

   _____

   _____

   _____

   _____

   _____

   _____

   _____

   _____

Name _____   Date _____

Instructor _____   Section _____

Experiment

11

Determination of Equilibrium Constant of an Indicator

> ## PURPOSE
>
> - Calculate the molar extinction coefficient ε of the protonated and unprotonated forms of bromocresol green
> - Determine experimentally the equilibrium constant (K_{In}) for bromocresol green, and compare the result with the theoretical K_{In} value

INTRODUCTION

An **indicator** is used to highlight the endpoint of a titration by changing color near the pH at which the stoichiometic endpoint of the reaction between acid and base is reached. For example:

$$HIn_{(aq)} \leftrightarrow H^+_{(aq)} + In^-_{(aq)} \qquad K_{In} = \frac{[H^+][In^-]}{[HIn]}$$

Yellow   Blue

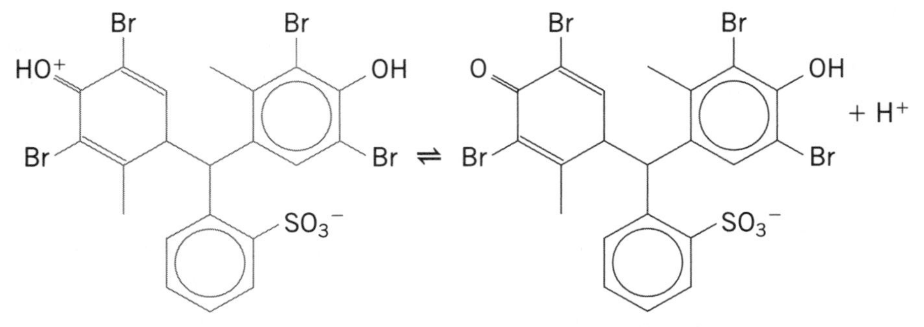

Figure 11.1

The protonated form of bromocresol green (HIn) is yellow. The loss of the proton results in the conjugate base form (In⁻), which is blue.

HIn (yellow)   In⁻ (blue)

Because indicators are weak acids themselves, they have acid and conjugate base pairs. The ratio of concentrations of these species at a given pH can be used to calculate the K_a of the indicator. Indicators have different chemical structures in the protonated and unprotonated form. It is the loss of the proton that is responsible for the color change. The protonated form has its own unique absorbance spectrum, as does the unprotonated form. As with any equilibrium system, all species must be present at equilibrium. When the absorbance of a sample of indicator is measured, this is the sum of the absorbances—from both the protonated and unprotonated forms—at the wavelength chosen. An aqueous solution of bromocresol green is green at pH 5.0 because it contains a mixture of both the protonated form, which is yellow, and the unprotonated form, which is blue. This experiment is designed so that you can decipher the amount of light absorbed by a sample of known pH at a given wavelength by each form of the indicator.

The absorbance of light at a given wavelength is directly proportional to concentration if the pathlength of the cuvette is constant. The absorbance is described by **Beer's Law**:

$$A = \varepsilon C l$$

where A is absorbance at a given wavelength; C is concentration in moles per liter; l is pathlength of cuvette in cm; and ε is the molar extinction coefficient in $M^{-1}cm^{-1}$, which is unique at each wavelength for each compound (a larger ε indicates that the compound absorbs more energy at this given wavelength).

Beer's Law is sometimes written as $A = abc$, where A is absorbance at a given wavelength, a the molar extinction coefficient, b the cuvette pathlength in cm, and c the solution concentration in molarity. *However, note:* this linear relationship is correct only when the absorbance is 2 or less.

Procedure Preview If bromocresol green is used as an indicator in an acid-strong base titration, a color change from yellow to blue will show the endpoint of the titration. To quantify the amount of the measured absorbance due to the protonated form of the indicator, a large excess of the strong acid HCl is added. Under these conditions, it is reasonable to assume that all of the indicator is protonated, thus allowing the absorbance of the light at this wavelength to be assigned to a known concentration of protonated indicator, HIn. Now the equation

$$\frac{A}{C} = \varepsilon l$$

can be used to calculate concentration. The pathlength, l, of the cuvettes used must be constant, but this is easy to ensure by treating another sample with a large excess of NaOH, so that

$$\frac{A}{C} = \varepsilon l$$

can also be calculated for In^-, the unprotonated form of the indicator. A buffer of known pH (therefore known $[H^+]$) is mixed with the indicator and, using the calculated extinction coefficients, $[H^+]$ is used to calculate K_{In}. Finally, the pH of a buffer solution will be determined.

1. What is an indicator? How does an indicator work?

_____

_____

_____

2. Look in your textbook, or a reference book like the *CRC* or the *Merck Index*, to find the theoretical K_{In} of bromocresol green.

_____

3. What is a buffer?

_____

_____

_____

4. Calculate the volume of 0.100 *M* sodium acetate that must be mixed with 20.00 mL of 0.100 *M* acetic acid to make a buffer of pH 4.30, assuming volumes are additive.

_____

_____

_____

_____

_____

_____

_____

5. Can bromocresol green be accurately used to show the endpoint of titration

   a. between the strong base NaOH and the strong acid HCl? Explain.

   b. between the strong base NaOH and the weak acid CH_3COOH? Explain.

_____

_____

_____

_____

_____

_____

MATERIALS

- device to measure 4.50 mL of solution (50-mL buret, 10-mL variable volume pipet, or 10-mL graduated cylinder)
- spectrophotometer (Spectronic 20 or colorimeter)
- cuvettes/test tubes (all of same or known pathlength; your instructor will explain how to test for consistent pathlength)
- ~5 × 10⁻⁵ M bromocresol green solution
- 0.10 M HCl
- 0.10 M NaOH
- distilled water
- pH meter
- standard pH buffers (of 4.00 and 10.00)
- 0.100 M acetic acid solution
- 0.100 M sodium acetate solution
- buffer of unknown pH
- parafilm
- stirring rod

PROCEDURE

I. Making Indicator and Buffer Solutions

Step A Place 4.50 mL of the bromocresol green solution in each of 6 test tubes.

Step B Add 4.50 mL of 0.100 M HCl to 2 test tubes already containing the indicator.

Step C Add 4.50 mL of 0.100 M NaOH to 2 test tubes already containing the indicator.

Step D Mix the solutions thoroughly by using a new transfer pipet for each sample (or tightly cover each test tube with a piece of parafilm and invert a few times).

Step E Make the buffer by mixing the appropriate volumes of 0.100 M acetic acid and 0.100 M sodium acetate, which you calculated in Pre-Lab Question 4.

Step F Calibrate the pH probe as directed by your teacher.

Step G Measure the pH of your buffer, taking time to let the reading become steady.

Step H Add 4.50 mL of your buffer to 2 test tubes, each containing 4.50 mL of bromocresol green indicator.

Step I Add 4.50 mL of the buffer of unknown pH to 2 test tubes, each containing 4.50 mL of bromocresol green indicator.

II. Measuring Absorbance

Step A Be sure that the spectrophotometer has warmed up for at least 20 minutes at 615 nm before continuing to Step B. If you are using a colorimeter, you need to assemble it before going to Step B.

Step B Calibrate the spectrophotometer or colorimeter as directed by your instructor. Be sure to use distilled water as a blank.

PROCEDURE
(continued)

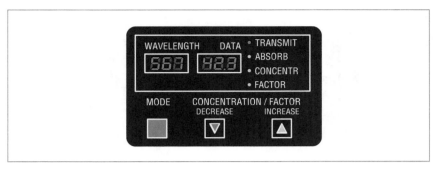

Figure 11.2 The spectrophotometer measures light intensities at variable wavelengths. Be sure the cuvette is clean and the sample solution clear before placing in the spectrophotometer.

Step C Fill a cuvette with each sample.

Step D Dip the cuvette in mild detergent solution, rinse and blot dry. Be sure the cuvette is clear of particulates or gas bubbles.

Step E Place the cuvette in the spectrophotometer (or colorimeter). Allow the absorbance reading to become constant before recording it.

Step F Repeat Step E for all samples.

Calculations

1. Present all your experimental data in tabular form.
2. Calculate the molar extinction coefficient (ε) of HIn, the protonated form of bromocresol green. Use the absorbance of the sample with excess acid, if you know the pathlength of the cuvette, or $\varepsilon_{HIn}l$ of these, if you do not know the pathlength.
3. Calculate the molar extinction coefficient (ε) of In^-, the unprotonated form of bromocresol green. Use the absorbance of the sample with excess base, if you know the pathlength of the cuvette, or $\varepsilon_{In^-}l$ of these, if you do not.
4. Set up two equations containing [HIn] and [In^-] and solve for each. You will need to use
   a. $A = \varepsilon_{HIn}l\,[HIn] + \varepsilon_{In^-}l[In^-]$ *and*
   b. your two calculated extinction coefficients; the absorbance of the buffer sample you made; and the fact that $[HIn]_0 = [In^-]_{eq} + [HIn]_{eq}$.
5. Calculate K_{In} for bromocresol green for each of the buffer solution/indicator mixtures.
6. Determine the pH of the unknown buffer. Use the relationships outlined in calculation 4; your K_{In} for bromocresol green; and the absorbance of the solution of bromocresol green and buffer of unknown pH in your calculations.
7. Compare your experimental constant for bromocresol green with the theoretical value.
8. Using your answer to calculation 5, propose and explain two possible sources of experimental error that would explain your actual results.

1. Why did the buffer used in this experiment to help determine the K_{In} have a pH of 4.30, and not of 9.00? Explain your answer in detail.

_____

_____

_____

_____

_____

_____

2. Would the pH of the buffer you made be more acidic, more basic, or the same if you had mistakenly added an additional 2.00 mL of sodium acetate solution? Thoroughly explain.

_____

_____

_____

_____

_____

_____

3. Would this experimental procedure need to be modified to find the K_{In} of phenolphthalein? Explain any changes that would need to be made in detail.

_____

_____

_____

_____

_____

_____

4. Could this experimental procedure be used to successfully determine the K_{In} of the **Universal Indicator**? Explain why or why not.

_____

_____

_____

_____

_____

_____

Experiment

12 Preparation of a Buffer Solution at a Given pH

> ## PURPOSE
> - Choose and make a buffer of given pH by dissolving known masses of solid salts in water
> - Make a buffer of given pH by mixing a predetermined volume of strong base with a salt solution

INTRODUCTION

A **buffer** keeps the pH of a substance stable by containing a component that will react with added acid or added base. Buffers in solution are common in everyday life and can be found in seawater, our blood, and many manufacturing processes and areas of scientific research. Buffers can also prevent food spoilage, or protein denaturation.

Because the acid and base in the buffer must coexist in solution and not react to neutralize each other, equilibrium between the acid and base part of the buffer must be established. So the buffer system must consist either of a weak acid (HA) and its conjugate base (A^-):

$$HA_{(aq)} \leftrightarrow H^+_{(aq)} + A^-_{(aq)} \qquad K_a = \frac{[H^+][A^-]}{[HA]} \qquad (1)$$

or of a weak base (B) and its conjugate acid (HB^+):

$$B_{(aq)} + H_2O_{(l)} \leftrightarrow HB^+_{(aq)} + OH^-_{(aq)} \qquad K_b = \frac{[HB^+][OH^-]}{[B]} \qquad (2)$$

By contrast, the mixture of a strong acid and a strong base reacts to stoichiometric completion, so that the remaining solution contains only the reactant in excess—not a mixture of acid and base—and consequently cannot act as a buffer to resist pH change.

Procedure Preview When approaching the question of what buffer system to use, you first must decide whether to work from the perspective of the acid (reaction 1) or the base (reaction 2). In this experiment you will begin by rolling dice to determine the pH of the buffer, so it is convenient to work in terms of [H^+], which is easier to calculate from the pH. Working from the perspective of the acid, then, you must next decide which weak acid to use as a buffer in the pH region that you have selected. To help in this determination, bear in mind that to be effective the concentrations of weak acid and conjugate base must be about equal in a buffer, that is, in a ratio of about 1. By rearranging the K_a expression

$$K_a = \frac{[H^+][A^-]}{[HA]} \quad \rightarrow \quad \frac{K_a}{[H^+]} = \frac{[A^-]}{[HA]}$$

and remembering that K_a is constant at any given temperature, it can be seen that the ratio of $[A^-]/[HA]$ determines the equilibrium $[H^+]$ concentration. Assuming a buffer is most effective when $0.1 < [A^-]/[HA] < 10$, the equilibrium equation can be simplified to

$$\text{buffer pH} = pK_a \pm 1$$

a formula that ensures that the ratio of acid to conjugate base will be in the range of 0.1 to 10. In other words, once the pH that you intend to buffer is given, you know you must have a weak acid whose pK_a is within 1 pUNIT of this pH. Having determined the weak acid to use, you must also verify that you have access to the conjugate base of that weak acid. (Be sure that the conjugate base is one proton removed from the acid.) Next, you need to determine the actual $[A^-]/[HA]$ ratio by solving

$$\frac{K_a}{[H^+]} = \frac{[A^-]}{[HA]}$$

Because the acid and its conjugate base are in the same solution, they must have the same volume. So the ratio of concentrations can be simplified into a ratio of moles.

Troubleshooting Buffers can be made by dissolving salts of the acid and conjugate base pair in water in the appropriate mole ratio. From Experiment 10, where you found the K_a of a weak acid, remember that one can titrate the acid part of the pair with a strong base, stopping at the appropriate pH. The procedure in this lab is a little harder to carry out, particularly if you must calculate the volume of base to add—not just add the base until the appropriate pH is reached. To calculate the volume, remember that all the conjugate base is formed in solution by neutralizing the acid with the base.

MATERIALS

- ➤ pH meter
- ➤ buret
- ➤ distilled water
- ➤ Erlenmeyer flasks
- ➤ balance
- ➤ solids to choose among:
  $NaHSO_3$, Na_2SO_3, $NaCH_3COO$, potassium hydrogen phthalate, Na_3PO_4, Na_2HPO_4, NaH_2PO_4, $KHCO_3$, K_2CO_3, Na_2SO_4, $NaHSO_4$, $NaHCO_3$, NaCl (*Note:* these salts may be hydrated, so pay careful attention to the actual formulas on the stock bottles.)

- ➤ weighing boats/papers
- ➤ scoopulas
- ➤ 2 dice (of distinct colors)
- ➤ solution: NaOH

PROCEDURE

I. Making Buffer Solution from Solid Salts

In this part of the lab you will first determine which salts to use to make your buffer of the given pH, then test and compare the experimental pH with the theoretical value.

Step A Roll the dice to pick the pH of the buffer you will make. Add 6 to the value of the first die to determine the magnitude of the pH (the characteristic). Use the number on the second die as the mantissa (number to the right of the decimal point). The pH must be greater than 6.0.

Record pH of the buffer you are making: _____

Step B Select your buffer system. Show all work you used to determine the acid/conjugate base pair chosen for making your buffer.

Step C Make the following calculations. Show all your work.

1. How many grams of each salt do you want to use to make 100 mL of your buffer?

2. Suppose, due to budget limits, you cannot use more than 5.0 grams of any salt to make 100 mL of buffer. Refine your calculations to meet this condition.

Step D Make your buffer. First write, then follow, the step-by-step procedure you will use.

Step E Research the theoretical pH of your buffer solution: _____

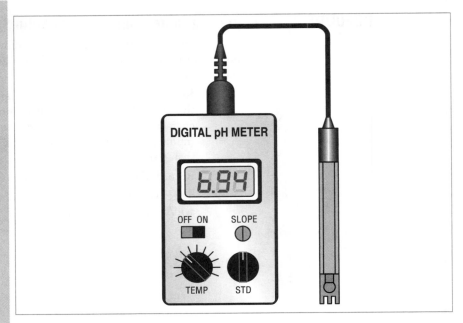

Figure 12.1

Step F Calibrate the pH meter. Your instructor will give you specific instructions.

Step G Rinse the pH meter tip with distilled water and pat it dry with paper towel. Place pH meter in solution, waiting for the reading to be steady.

Record the actual pH of your buffer solution: _____

II. Making Buffer by Adding a Known Volume of Strong Base to a Salt Solution

In this part of the lab you will be making a buffer at your determined pH by mixing 100 mL of a 0.050 M solution of one of your salts with a known volume of _____ M NaOH.

Step A Roll the dice. Record the pH of the buffer you are making:

_____

Step B Make the following calculations. Show all your work.

1. Which salt will you use to make the solution? Write one sentence explaining why you chose this salt.

_____

_____

2. How many grams of salt will you need to make 100 mL of 0.050 M solution?

3. How many milliliters of the NaOH solution will you need to add to make a buffer for your desired pH?

PROCEDURE
(continued)

Step C Using the mass of the salt from Step B2 above, make 100 mL of your 0.050 *M* solution.

Step D Rinse the pH meter tip with distilled water and pat dry with paper towel. Place the pH meter in your 0.050 *M* salt solution and wait for the reading to be constant.

Record the pH of this salt solution: _____

Step E Using the buret, add the desired volume of the base to your solution and mix thoroughly. This volume was determined in Step B3 above.

Step F Rinse the pH meter tip with distilled water and pat it dry with paper towel.

Step G Place the pH meter in your 0.050 *M* salt solution and wait for the reading to be constant.

Record the pH of your buffer solution: _____

Post-Lab Questions

1. Propose two reasons why the actual pH of your buffer solution might not be identical to the theoretical pH. Explain in detail how these errors would lead to the pH you obtained. For example: Why is the actual pH more basic than the theoretical? (Calculation errors are not acceptable as an explanation.)

_____

_____

_____

_____

_____

_____

_____

_____

_____

_____

_____

_____

_____

_____

_____

_____

_____

_____

_____

_____

Post-Lab Questions *(continued)*

2. What would happen to the pH of your buffer if it were diluted with 100 mL of distilled water? Assume volumes are additive.

Name _____   Date _____

Instructor _____   Section _____

Experiment

13   Kinetics: Differential and Integrated Rate Laws

> ## PURPOSE
>
> - Observe and compare the effects of homogeneous and heterogeneous catalysts on the decomposition of hydrogen peroxide
> - Measure reaction rates to determine the order of reaction with respect to various reactants
> - Analyze experimental data to write a differential rate law expression
> - Analyze decay data to determine the integrated rate law constant for a radioactive substance

INTRODUCTION

The study of the rates of chemical reactions is called **kinetics**. Reactions are altered by a number of factors that may be exploited to control their rates. A kineticist will study these factors for a given reaction, considering them as a means to control the rate of the reaction so that it might be studied thoroughly in the laboratory or, possibly, monitored for effectiveness as an industrial process.

On a molecular basis, the collision theory of chemical reactions predicts that reacting particles must collide in a particular way to allow a reaction to occur. The collision will be an effective one only if the reacting particles collide with sufficient kinetic energy to allow rupture of any existing bond. Further, the reacting particles must strike each other in an orientation that allows a new chemical bond to form. Only if both of these criteria are met will an effective collision occur and a chemical reaction ensue. The vast majority of these collisions between potentially reacting particles are ineffective and do not lead to a chemical reaction. A step-by-step description of the process on a molecular level is called a **reaction mechanism**.

There are a number of factors that alter reaction rate. These include:

> ➤ concentration
> ➤ temperature
> ➤ chemical characteristics
> ➤ surface area of reactants
> ➤ presence of a catalyst

Each of these characteristics may alter the rate of reaction. Increasing the *concentration* of a substance means that more particles are available to collide, potentially leading to more effective collisions. Increasing the *temperature* of a system should cause a greater fraction of reacting particles to carry enough kinetic energy to break existing bonds. Some reactants are more likely to react quickly because of *chemical characteristics*; for example, the metal magnesium is more reactive than the metal iron. Although a piece of magnesium will burst into spectacularly bright flame if introduced to a Bunsen burner flame, a similar piece of iron will merely glow red if placed in the same flame. To cause a reaction as dramatic as that of magnesium, the red-hot iron might be dropped into a container of pure oxygen. Or, the *surface area* of the iron—another factor affecting reaction rate—might be increased greatly. As an example of this factor, a piece of steel wool burns much more readily that does the same mass of iron in the form of a solid piece.

Finally, the rate of a chemical reaction may be altered by a ***catalyst***, a substance that is not itself consumed in the reaction. Most catalysts cause an increase in the rate of reaction. Some cause the opposite effect and slow the chemical reaction. These negative catalysts are called **inhibitors**. In general, catalysts fall into two groups, depending on phase: **homogeneous** catalysts are found in the same phase as the reacting substances, whereas **heterogeneous** catalysts are in a different phase.

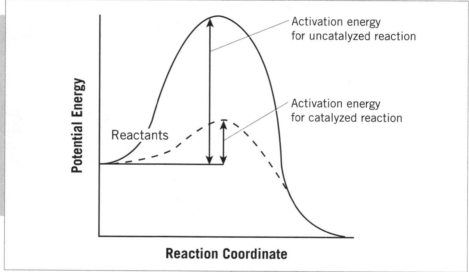

Figure 13.1

A catalyst alters the pathway of a chemical reaction so that the alternate path has a lower activation energy, and more rapid reaction rate, than the uncatalyzed reaction.

Because the rate of a chemical reaction is influenced by the concentration of the reactants, a rate law can be developed to quantify the relationship. The rate law follows the general form

$$\text{Rate} = k\,[\text{reactant A}]^x\,[\text{reactant B}]^y$$

where x and y are the orders of the reactants. A reactant is said to be **first order** if a change in its concentration causes a direct corresponding change in the rate of reaction; hence doubling the concentration would cause a doubling of the reaction rate. A **second order** reactant causes an exponential change; hence, doubling the concentration of a second order reactant will cause a 2^2, or fourfold, increase in the reaction rate. Changing the concentration of a **zero order** reactant causes no change in the reaction rate. The order of a reaction must be determined experimentally and cannot be gleaned from the coefficients of a balanced chemical equation.

Procedure Preview In this lab, you will develop kinetics data for two kinds of rate laws. First, data for **differential rate law** will be determined experimentally by altering the concentrations of reactants in a predictable fashion, then measuring the changes in *initial rates* that occur as a result of the changes in concentration. Thus multiple trials are required. The behavior of each trial is compared to that of the other trials as you calculate the order of each reactant in the equation.

Data for **integrated rate law** are to be determined in a different way. Only a single trial is required and the concentration of a reactant is measured at different times. The results of those measurements are then plotted in several ways to determine the order of a reactant. A first-order reactant A will give a straight line if the natural log of the concentration of A is plotted versus time:

$$\ln[A]_t - \ln[A]_o = -kt \ \text{ or}$$

$$kt = \ln\left(\frac{[A]_o}{[A]_t}\right)$$

Note that the slope of the line is equal to the opposite of k.

A second-order reactant A will give a straight line if inverse concentration of A is plotted versus time:

$$\frac{1}{[A]_t} - \frac{1}{[A]_o} = kt$$

Note that the slope of this line is equal to k.

A zero-order reactant A will give a straight line if $[A]$ versus time is plotted and the slope of the line is equal to the opposite of k.

Table 13.1

Summary of kinetics for reaction of reactant R until time t
(or $R_0 \rightarrow R_t$)

Characteristic	If Zero Order	If First Order	If Second Order
Differential rate law	Rate = $k\,[R]^0$	Rate = $k\,[R]^1$	Rate = $k\,[R]^2$
Integrated rate law	$[R]_t = -kt + [R]_0$	$\ln[R]_t = -kt + \ln[R]_0$	$\frac{1}{[R]} = kt + \frac{1}{[R]_0}$
Straight line graph	$[R]$ vs t	$\ln[R]$ vs t	$\frac{1}{[R]}$ vs t
k and slope m of line	$m = -k$	$m = -k$	$m = k$
Halflife $t_{\frac{1}{2}}$	$t_{\frac{1}{2}} = \frac{[R]_0}{2k}$	$t_{\frac{1}{2}} = \frac{0.693}{k}$	$t_{\frac{1}{2}} = \frac{1}{k[R]_0}$

PART A: Differential Rate Law: Catalyzed Decomposition of H_2O_2

In this part of the lab, you will study the effects of different kinds of catalysts on the decomposition of hydrogen peroxide by employing two different methods. In the first method, the mineral pyrolusite will provide a convenient surface for the decomposition of the hydrogen peroxide. This mineral is a heterogeneous catalyst, and its pitted surface provides an attractive site for the reaction to occur. In the second method, a homogeneous catalyst, a solution of potassium iodide, will be used. In this case, the iodide in the KI is actually involved in the chemistry of the reaction. However, because the KI is regenerated and found in the same form in which it originally existed, it meets the criteria to be considered a catalyst.

Hydrogen peroxide is unstable and **disproportionates** easily to form water and oxygen gas over time. Disproportionation changes a substance, with oxidation and reduction occurring concurrently. In this reaction, oxygen changes from an oxidation number of -1 in the peroxide ion to a zero oxidation number, as the elemental form of oxygen gas, and to a -2 oxidation number, as oxygen combined with hydrogen in the water molecule.

$$2\ H_2O_{2(aq)} \rightarrow 2\ H_2O_{(l)} + O_{2(g)}$$

This reaction is slow, but it is commonly catalyzed using manganese(IV) oxide. Using a simple apparatus, the rate of the decomposition can be monitored on the small scale by counting the number of oxygen bubbles formed during a certain time period. This count will serve as a measure of the rate of formation of oxygen. It is assumed that the pressure inside the reaction flask builds to a constant level. After that pressure is reached, the number of bubbles produced in the water at the small tip within the reservoir is a direct result of additional oxygen generated in the flask by the decomposition of the hydrogen peroxide.

Method 1: Heterogeneous Catalyst

$$H_2O_{2(aq)} \xrightarrow{\text{pyrolusite}} H_2O_{(l)} + O_{2(g)}$$

You will perform this experiment using five solutions of H_2O_2 (10% initially, then diluted to 5%, to 3.3%, to 2.5%, and to 1%). You will then graph log rate (bubbles per second) versus log concentration (% H_2O_2) to obtain the reaction order with respect to H_2O_2.

Because this is a decomposition reaction and the catalyst does not appear in the rate law,

$$\text{rate} = k[H_2O_2]^x$$

Taking the log of both sides of the equation yields

$$\log \text{rate} = \log k + x \log [H_2O_2]$$

$$\log \text{rate} = x \log [H_2O_2] + \log k$$

If you graph this relationship, note that the plot will take the familiar form of a linear equation

$$y = mx + b$$

where $y = \log$ rate, $x = \log [H_2O_2]$, the y-intercept $b = \log k$, and $m = x$, the order of the H_2O_2. For this reason, determining the slope of the line that you plot will allow you to determine the order of the hydrogen peroxide in this decomposition reaction.

MATERIALS

➤ 50-mL Erlenmeyer flask
➤ one-hole rubber stopper attachment, containing Beral pipet bulb and micropipet tip insert *(see Appendix E on page 144)*
➤ pyrolusite
➤ 10% H_2O_2 solution (diluted to 5%, 3.3%, 2.5% and 1.0% solutions)
➤ microstir bar *(see Appendix C on page 140)*
➤ magnetic stir plate
➤ 10-mL graduated cylinder
➤ distilled water

PROCEDURE

Step A Ready the following materials:
  • 50-mL Erlenmeyer flask
  • piece of pyrolusite approximately the size of a finger tip
  • reservoir apparatus made from a Beral pipet bulb, micropipet tip and one-hole rubber stopper

Step B Use forceps to place the piece of pyrolusite and the magnetic stir bar in the flask, and place flask on magnetic stirrer so stir bar will not hit the piece of pyrolusite. (Do not touch the pyrolusite with your fingers because the oils from your skin will adversely affect the catalyst.) Turn on the magnetic stir plate to test the placement of the stir bar and the catalyst. Reposition if needed.

Step C Dilute 10% hydrogen peroxide to make 10.0 mL of the appropriate H_2O_2 solution in a graduated cylinder. The 5% solution will require 5 mL 10% solution and 5 mL distilled water, and so on.

Step D Add this solution to the flask and quickly place the reservoir apparatus securely on top of the flask. Quickly fill the bulb more than ½ full with distilled water and insert securely into the mouth of the Erlenmeyer flask. Swirl the flask to mix the solution and wash it across the pyrolusite. Wait 30–45 seconds, until bubbles begin to appear regularly. Then count the number of oxygen bubbles released during a two-minute period. (*Hint:* for an accurate count of bubbles released, record each bubble by keeping a running tally on paper.)

Step E Repeat with the other concentrations of hydrogen peroxide.

Calculations (Method 1)

1. Present all your data in tabular form.
2. Represent your total number of bubbles counted as a rate of bubbles/minute.
3. On graphing paper, plot your results to determine the reaction order with respect to H_2O_2. Perform a regression line analysis on the points. The slope of this line will be the order of the reaction with respect to the hydrogen peroxide.

Method 2: Homogeneous Catalyst

For the reaction

$$2\,H_2O_{2(aq)} \xrightarrow{\text{KI catalyst}} 2\,H_2O_{(l)} + O_{2(g)}$$

the rate depends both on the $[H_2O_2]$ and $[KI]$. You will measure the rate of formation of O_2 gas by counting the number of O_2 gas bubbles that are released during a 3-minute period. You will vary the concentrations of H_2O_2 and KI in a systematic way to determine the reaction order with respect to each.

MATERIALS

> ➤ 50-mL Erlenmeyer flask
> ➤ one-hole rubber stopper attachment (containing Beral pipet bulb and micropipet tip insert)
> ➤ 10% H_2O_2
> ➤ 0.1 *M* KI
> ➤ distilled water
> ➤ microstir bar
> ➤ magnetic stir plate
> ➤ 10-mL graduated cylinder

PROCEDURE

Step A Use the same apparatus with a magnetic stir bar as in Method 1, but without pyrolusite. Add the appropriate volumes of H_2O and 0.1 *M* KI to the flask, as outlined in Table 13.2, then add the H_2O_2.

Step B Place the bubbling lid securely on top of the flask, quickly fill it 2/3 up with distilled water, and cover. Begin swirling flask to mix, and wait about 30–45 seconds.

Step C Begin counting the number of oxygen bubbles that are released during a three-minute period. (*Hint:* to help keep count of bubbles released, run a tally on a piece of paper.)

Step D Repeat for all ratios of reactants outlined in Table 13.2.

Table 13.2 Dilution Scheme for Reactants

Trial	Volume 10 % H_2O_2 (mL)	Volume H_2O (mL)	Volume KI (mL)
1	2.0	14.0	4.0
2	4.0	12.0	4.0
3	2.0	10.0	8.0

Because the total volume is 20.0 mL in each case, the concentrations of each are proportional to the volumes added.

Calculations (Method 2)

1. Present all your data in tabular form.
2. Represent your total number of bubbles counted as a rate of bubbles/minute.
3. Write a generic rate law expression and determine algebraically the reaction order, with respect both to H_2O_2 and KI, using relative rates.

Post-Lab Questions

1. Why is it important to stir the solution in each reaction? Explain what would happen to your experimental results if you did not stir the solution in each case.

_____

_____

_____

_____

_____

_____

_____

_____

_____

2. Do the two catalysts, pyrolusite and KI, work in the same manner to increase the rate of decomposition? Use evidence from your experimental results to prove your response.

_____

_____

_____

_____

_____

_____

_____

_____

_____

3. What would happen to the rate of bubble formation in Method 1 if the pyrolusite were ground into a powder rather than in chunk form?

_____

_____

_____

_____

_____

_____

_____

_____

_____

PART B: Integrated Rate Law: Kinetics of Radioactive Decay

In this second part of the lab, you will be working from radiation count data taken from a sample of phosphorus-32, a radioactive substance.

Nuclei that have an unstable ratio of neutrons to protons revert to a more stable configuration by emitting various particles, as well as energy in the form of gamma radiation. Radioactive decay is always a first-order process. First-order reactants have a characteristic half-life that does not change over time. Note that there is a convenient relationship between the rate constant k and the half-life $t_{\frac{1}{2}}$:

$$kt = \ln\left(\frac{[A]}{_o}\right)$$

$$k\,t_{\frac{1}{2}} = \ln\left(\frac{[1]}{[0.5]}\right) = \ln(2)$$

$$k\,t_{\frac{1}{2}} = 0.693$$

There are four types of nuclear transmutations, any of which can change the identity of a nucleus:

> **beta** ($^0_{-1}\beta$, equivalent to an electron)
> **positron** ($^0_{+1}e$, a positively charged electron)
> **alpha** ($^4_2\alpha$, a helium nucleus stripped of its two electrons)
> **electron-capture** (an electron attracted into the nucleus from the electron cloud surrounding that nucleus)

Because these processes change the mass and/or charge of a nucleus, they must be included in a nuclear equation. Another type of emission, the **gamma ray**, changes the energy balance of a nucleus, but, because it does not change the mass or charge of a nucleus, it is not included in a nuclear equation. Nuclear equations are easy to write and balance as long as you remember that there must be conservation of mass (all the atomic numbers on each side must add to the same total) *and* conservation of charge (all the charge numbers on each side must add to the same total).

Examples of nuclear equations:

Alpha:	$^{238}_{92}U \rightarrow {}^4_2\alpha + {}^{234}_{90}Th$
Beta:	$^{234}_{90}Th \rightarrow {}^{234}_{91}Pa + {}^0_{-1}\beta$
Positron:	$^{11}_6C \rightarrow {}^{11}_5B + {}^0_{+1}e$
Electron capture:	$^{81}_{37}Rb + {}^0_{-1}e \rightarrow {}^{81}_{36}Kr$

MATERIALS

> Geiger counter
> sample of phosphorus-32*

Alternative to P-32 sample:
> data from Table 13.3

*CAUTION: In general, schools are encouraged **not** to use radioactive isotopes, even low-energy beta emitters like P-32. To allow analysis of data without taking counts directly from a radioactive substance, a sample of data taken by high school students in the past is provided in Table 13.3. Familiarize yourself with these data before proceeding to the Post-Lab Calculations and Questions.

Copyright © Peoples Publishing Group. Photocopying not permitted.

PROCEDURE

Step A Use the Geiger counter to establish a background count of cosmic radiation by pointing the sensor away from the P-32. Note the count in counts per minute as "CPM background."

Step B Take a one-minute count of the P-32 by pointing the sensor of the Geiger counter directly at the sample. Repeat and average the two readings. Record as "CPM average."

Table 13.3 Data for Determining Half-life of P-32

Date	Time of observation	Time since start	CPM average	CPM background	CPM from sample
Jan. 21	9:15 A.M.	0 minutes	52051	31	52020
Jan. 25	8:15 A.M.		44504	28	
Jan. 26	8:45 A.M.		42942	41	
Jan. 27	8:05 A.M.		40967	39	
Jan. 28	9:07 A.M.		39179	37	
Jan. 29	8:00 A.M.		38800	36	
Jan. 30	11:40 A.M.		36565	34	
Feb. 1	10:00 A.M.		33630	35	
Feb. 2	8:00 A.M.		32204	36	
Feb. 3	9:08 A.M.		31154	45	
Feb. 4	8:30 A.M.		29694	34	
Feb. 5	10:15 A.M.		28244	28	
Feb. 6	11:30 A.M.		27449	41	
Feb. 9	12:30 P.M.		24246	24	
Feb. 10	9:05 A.M.		23059	28	
Feb. 11	9:07 A.M.		21976	40	
Feb. 15	8:51 A.M.		18657	40	
Feb. 16	9:00 A.M.		17992	25	
Feb. 17	9:00 A.M.		16912	30	
Feb. 18	9:00 A.M.		15970	33	
Feb. 19	9:15 A.M.		15580	26	
Feb. 20	12:00 A.M.		15002	37	
Feb. 22	10:30 A.M.		13821	30	
Feb. 24	8:00 A.M.		12568	28	
Feb. 29	9:30 A.M.		10250	34	
Mar. 2	11:10 A.M.		9153	25	
Mar. 3	9:42 A.M.		8900	27	
Mar. 4	9:00 A.M.		8536	39	
Mar. 5	11:30 A.M.		7911	26	
Mar. 7	10:05 A.M.		7389	31	
Mar. 9	2:00 P.M.		6646	26	

PROCEDURE
(continued)

Calculations (Part B)

1. Calculate "Time since start" by comparing "Time of observation" with the original observation on January 21. Calculate "CPM from sample" by subtracting "CPM background" from "CPM average."
2. Graph the data. Counts per minute (CPM) and concentration [C] are directly proportional. Because radioactive decay must be first order kinetics,

$$\ln(CPM) = -kt$$

and the plot of ln(CPM) versus time will be a straight line. Make a best-fit straight line to fit your data and determine the slope of that line.
3. Show how the value of the rate constant k and the half-life $t_{\frac{1}{2}}$ can be determined from the results of your graph.

Post-Lab Questions

1. Which units did you select for each axis of your graph? Why? How many significant figures may you employ in your calculated half-life? Explain.

2. Are there health risks involved in dealing with P-32? Explain.

3. What type of radioactive decay does P-32 undergo? Explain. Write a nuclear equation to describe the decay.

4. What is a Geiger counter and how does it work?

5. How long does it take for 50% of a sample of P-32 to decay? 95%? 99%?

6. Germanium-66 is a positron emitter with $t_{\frac{1}{2}} = 9.4$ hr.
   a. Write a balanced nuclear equation.

   b. How much Ge-66 remains of a 1.00 g sample after 25.0 hr?

Copyright © Peoples Publishing Group. Photocopying not permitted.

102 | Laboratory Investigations: AP Chemistry

Name _____   Date _____

Instructor _____   Section _____

Experiment

14

Determining Molar Mass by Freezing Point Depression

PURPOSE
- Compare freezing points of a pure solvent and a known solution of the solvent to determine the change in freezing point, ΔT_f
- Calculate the molal freezing point depression constant (K_f) for the solvent
- Determine the molar mass of an unknown solute using data from the preceding procedures

INTRODUCTION

A **solution** is a homogeneous mixture of substances, comprised of at least two components, the major component being the solvent and the minor the solute. The **solvent** is the component that defines the phase of a solution; it is the material into which the solute is introduced. The **solute** is the substance that dissolves in a solvent to form a solution. A solution can be made from any combination of the phases of matter. In this lab, two solids are mixed together, then melted to complete the solution process.

There are a number of ways of expressing concentration quantitatively, but the ones commonly used in AP Chemistry are molarity (M), molality (m), mole fraction (χ), and mass percent. These are defined as follows:

$$M = \frac{\text{mol solute}}{\text{L solution}}$$

$$m = \frac{\text{mol solute}}{\text{kg solvent}}$$

$$\chi = \frac{\text{mol solute}}{(\text{total number of mol solute} + \text{mol solvent})}$$

$$\text{mass \%} = \frac{\text{mass solute}}{(\text{total mass solute} + \text{solvent}) \times 100}$$

Because volume varies as temperature varies, any concentration measure that includes volume in its definition is temperature dependent. Therefore, a stated molarity, for instance, must include the temperature at which the solution was measured. Ratios that compare only moles or mass are not temperature dependent, because those quantities do not vary as the temperature does.

Colligative properties are a set of characteristics that differ for a pure solvent and a solution of the solvent. The presence of particles of solute in the solvent interferes with the normal behavior of the solvent, especially the characteristic of vapor pressure. It is not important what the chemical composition or size of the solute particles may be, just that they are in solution with the solvent. It is the *quantity of particles* in solution that does change the behavior of the solvent, so a measure of concentration occurs in each of the equations that describe colligative properties. These equations describe the behavior of dilute solutions best, because the behavior of dilute solutions is closest to ideal. At higher concentrations the solutions no longer behave in an ideal fashion.

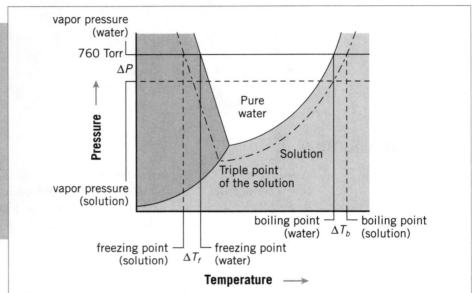

Figure 14.1

This generic phase diagram illustrates change in three colligative properties—vapor pressure (ΔP), freezing point (ΔT_f), and boiling point (ΔT_b)— for pure water vs. an aqueous solution.

The colligative property investigated in this lab is that of **freezing point depression**. The presence of solute particles extends the temperature range over which the solvent remains liquid, so the boiling point of the solution is higher than that of the solvent, whereas the freezing point of the solution is lower than that of the solvent. The equation that describes the change in freezing point is

$$\Delta T_f = iK_f m$$

where
i = number of moles of solute particles in solution (van't Hoff value)
K_f = molal freezing point constant for the solvent
m = concentration in molality (used since temperature varies)

Procedure Preview In this experiment, you will establish the freezing point of a pure solvent. By contaminating the pure solvent with a known quantity of a known solute, you can formulate a known solution. Then, by determining the freezing point of the known solution and comparing it to the freezing point of the pure solvent, you will be able to calculate the change in freezing point, ΔT_f, and the freezing point depression constant, K_f, of the solvent. Finally, by making a solution of a fresh sample of the solvent with an unknown solute, and measuring its freezing point, you can calculate the molar mass of the unknown solute. You will make use of the following equations:

$$\Delta T_f = iK_f m$$

$$m = \frac{\text{mol solute}}{\text{kg solvent}}$$

$$\text{mol solute} = \frac{\text{g solute}}{MM \text{ solute}}$$

By substituting, you can derive this relationship:

$$MM_{solute} = \frac{iK_f (\text{solvent})g_{solute}}{\text{kg solvent } \Delta T_f}$$

MATERIALS

➤ medium test tubes
➤ lauric acid (dodecanoic acid, $CH_3(CH_2)_{10}COOH$)
➤ palmitic acid (hexadecanoic acid, $CH_3(CH_2)_{14}COOH$)
➤ unknown molecular solute
➤ thermometer (*or* thermoprobe with CBL or computer)
➤ hot water bath (*Lab Hint:* start the bath *now* because it will be used several times during the experiment. One hundred mL of tap water in a 250-mL beaker is more than enough.)

Optional
➤ ring stand and clamp

PROCEDURE

I. Establishing the freezing point of the pure solvent

Step A Weigh out >5 g of lauric acid. Although your quantity need not be exactly 5 g, it is important to record how much you do use.

Step B Place the lauric acid into a medium test tube.

Step C Transfer the test tube to the hot water bath, submerging the closed end of the tube into the hot water.

Step D When the lauric acid has melted completely, move the test tube out of the hot water bath. You could clamp the test tube to a ring stand, but it may be just as convenient to hold it.

Step E Place a thermometer (or thermoprobe) into the solvent.

Step F Read the temperature of the liquid lauric acid every 15 seconds for 5 minutes, or until the temperature has not changed for two minutes. Record the temperature to 0.1°C. Do not use the temperature-sensing device to stir, but move it often so that the temperature measured is that of the center of a well-mixed liquid solution.

II. Establishing K_f of the solvent using known solute

Step A Weigh out <0.5 g of palmitic acid. Although the quantity need not be exactly 0.5 g, it is important to record exactly how much you measure out.

Step B Add the palmitic acid directly into the test tube that contains the lauric acid used in Procedure I above.

Step C Transfer the test tube to the hot water bath, submerging the closed end of the tube until the solution melts completely.

Step D Establish the freezing point of the solution, as you did for the pure solvent.

Step E Be sure to clean the temperature-sensing device by rinsing it in hot water, then wiping it carefully with a paper towel.

III. Determining *MM* of the unknown solute

Step A Prepare a new test tube of solvent by weighing out a fresh sample of >5 g of lauric acid.

Step B Weigh out <0.5 g of an unknown solute, to be specified by your instructor. Add the solute to the lauric acid in the new test tube.

Step C Melt the solution completely in the hot water bath, taking temperature readings every 15 seconds, as in the previous procedures, until the freezing point of the solution of lauric acid + unknown solute is established.
(***Caution:*** Do ***not*** pour hot solutions into the sink! They will solidify in the trap and block the drain. Ask your instructor for explicit directions on how to dispose of the waste.)

Calculations

1. Using a graphing program, draw graphs of the three cooling curves (pure lauric acid, lauric acid + palmitic acid, lauric acid + unknown solute). Be sure to plot temperature on the *y*-axis and time on the *x*-axis.
2. Find a freezing point for each curve by drawing two lines—one tangential to the curve where it represents the liquid cooling rapidly, and one tangential to the curve where it represents the liquid-solid slurry (the plateau of the graph). The point of intersection of these two tangents is the freezing point.
3. Determine ΔT_f by comparing the cooling curves for pure lauric acid and the lauric acid-palmitic acid solution.
4. Use ΔT_f, and *m* (the molality) to calculate the K_f (molal freezing point depression constant) for the solvent lauric acid.
5. Determine ΔT_f by comparing the cooling curves for the pure lauric acid and the solution of lauric acid + unknown solute.
6. Use this ΔT_f and the K_f established in Calculation 4 to figure the *MM* of the unknown solute.

1. If the unknown solute were benzoic acid, what would be the percent error in the calculated *MM*? Look up the term **dimerization** and comment on its application in this lab.

_____

_____

_____

_____

_____

_____

_____

_____

_____

_____

_____

_____

_____

2. Use the *Merck Index*, the *CRC Handbook of Chemistry and Physics*, *Lange's Handbook of Chemistry*, or another reference source to find a published value for the freezing point of lauric acid. Calculate percent error. Comment on possible sources of error. Would an error in establishing the freezing point of lauric acid affect the results of your attempt to find the *MM* of the unknown?

_____

_____

_____

_____

_____

_____

_____

_____

_____

_____

_____

_____

_____

Post-Lab Questions *(continued)*

3. In each of the following cases, explain your reasoning thoroughly, using equations if necessary. What would have happened to your calculated *MM* if you had

   a. spilled some lauric acid before finding the freezing point?

   b. spilled some palmitic acid before adding it to the lauric acid?

   c. failed to clean lauric acid–palmitic acid solution from the temperature-sensing device before measuring the lauric acid–unknown solution?

Experiment

15 Chromatography of a Popular Consumer Beverage

PURPOSE

- Use paper chromatography to separate the food dyes in a popular colored beverage
- Determine the identities of the dyes in food coloring, using the known dyes in the popular consumer beverage as standards

INTRODUCTION

A **mixture** is a physical phenomenon, a combination of two or several substances. Because each component of a mixture retains its chemical identity and characteristics, a mixture can be separated into its chemical components by exploiting physical differences. For example, suppose that you were given the task of separating a mixture of bowling balls and Ping-Pong balls. This mixture might be sifted with a volleyball net to exploit the physical characteristic of *size*: the bowling balls being held within the net, while the smaller Ping-Pong balls passed through the openings. Or, you might exploit the physical characteristic of *density* by pouring your mixture of balls into a swimming pool and noting that the bowling balls sink to the bottom of the pool, while the less dense Ping-Pong balls stay at the surface. You might also exploit the physical characteristic of *color* by separating the white Ping-Pong balls from the darker bowling balls. In each case, you have identified a physical difference between or among the components of a mixture and used that characteristic to sort those components.

One laboratory method of separation is called **chromatography**, from the Greek *chroma*, meaning "color," and *graphein*, meaning "to write." The method depends on the tendencies of different components of a mixture to have varying degrees of adsorption onto solid surfaces. In general, chromatographic methods work by using a combination of two phases of matter, commonly one in the solid state and one in the liquid state. The solid represents the **stationary phase**, while the liquid (or, sometimes, a gas) represents the **mobile phase**. Typically a liquid mixture of components is passed over a solid, and the difference in relative attraction of each liquid for the solid can be used to separate those components physically. A component with little attraction for the solid will pass quickly by the surface of the solid, whereas a substance with greater attraction for the surface of the solid will linger longer. There are a variety of types of chromatography, but all exploit the characteristic of preferential adsorption onto a solid surface. Methods include thin-layer chromatography and gas chromatography.

One popular type of chromatography is **paper chromatography**. A strip of filter or other porous paper is used as the stationary phase. A concentrated spot of the mixture to be separated is dotted onto the lower end of the paper strip. The end of the paper strip is then dipped into the mobile phase, which is a mixture of liquid solvents. The liquid phase gets wicked up the strip of paper and, in so doing, passes by the dot of the mixture, attracting its components and moving the dot up the paper. Different components of the mixture are carried different distances up the paper. Components with little attraction for the solid paper are carried farther up than those components that adsorb better onto the paper. The liquid solvent mixture can be altered to change its rate of movement up the solid phase.

To measure the differences in adsorption onto a solid surface, you may determine a value called the R_f, or **r**atio of **f**ronts. The R_f is a ratio that compares the distance traveled by a component of the mixture to the distance traveled by the solvent:

$$R_f \, (component) = \frac{D_{spot\,front}}{D_{solvent\,front}}$$

where $D_{spot\,front}$ indicates the distance traveled by the front of the spot of the component of the mixture being considered and $D_{solvent\,front}$ represents the farthest distance traveled by the solvent. Note that R_f values are characteristic of a solute-solvent combination under specified conditions. Changing the temperature of the system, for example, or the material of the solid phase, may change the value of the R_f.

You may have used paper chromatography in your biology class to separate chlorophyll into its components, chlorophyll a and chlorophyll b.

Procedure Preview In this experiment you will take a concentrated solution made from a powdered beverage containing known food dyes, and use these dyes as standards in a chromatography experiment to determine the identity of the dyes in food coloring. The ingredients in food colorings are normally listed on the outside of the box containing a variety of different colors; however, this list does not break down the specific dyes in each individual food coloring. But each powdered beverage does show the specific list of food colors it contains, so you can separate them using paper chromatography and a solvent system, or a developing solution, containing a mixture of aqueous ammonia, ethanol, and isopropanol, and then use the results as standards. The identity of the food dyes in the food coloring can be determined by comparing the distance that each individual food dye in the food coloring traveled on the paper to the distance that the standard food dyes in the powdered beverage solution moved on the paper.

Pre-Lab Questions

1. From your teacher, obtain a list of food dyes in the powdered beverage and in the food coloring samples you will use in your experiment. Find their chemical structures in the *Merck Index* or other chemical database. Draw the structures of each food dye.

2. Read through all the steps of the Procedures below. Why do you think the development chamber must be sealed during this experiment? How fast would the experiment proceed if a student forgot to seal the development chamber?

   _____

   _____

   _____

3. Why do we use a pencil to mark chromatography paper, rather than a ballpoint or felt-tipped pen? What would happen if we used one of these pens instead?

   _____

   _____

   _____

MATERIALS

➤ samples of food colorings
➤ powdered beverage mixes (each containing known food dyes)
➤ scoopulas/spoons
➤ chromatography paper (alternatively, Whatman Number 1 filter paper)
➤ ruler, pencil, & stapler
➤ toothpicks
➤ 24-well microplate
➤ developing solution (consisting of 50 mL household ammonia, 25 mL 70% isopropanol, 25 mL 91% ethanol)
➤ 600-mL beaker (as developing chamber)
➤ plastic wrap/parafilm (to seal developing chamber)

PROCEDURE

I. Preparing solutions of powdered beverage and the chromatography paper

Step A Carefully add enough powdered beverage mix to specific wells in the microplate, being sure not to contaminate surrounding wells with other samples. Record the well to which each sample is added. Use a clean and dry scoopula or spoon for each sample.

Step B Add enough hot water to fill each well containing a sample about two-thirds full, then use a new toothpick to mix and dissolve each sample in the hot water.

Step C Cut chromatography paper into a 10-cm × 20-cm rectangle. The 20-cm side is the horizontal axis.

Step D Use a pencil to lightly draw a straight line 1 cm from the bottom of the rectangle. Draw two other lines, each 1 cm from the rectangle sides.

Step E Lightly mark the bottom line every 2 cm; these marks are where you will spot the paper with each sample. Lightly number each mark underneath the horizontal line with the pencil.

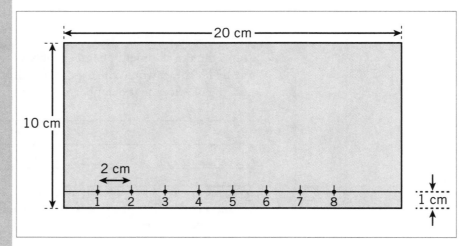

Figure 15.1

PROCEDURE
(continued)

II. Spotting chromatography paper with samples and developing the sample

Step A Using a new toothpick for each sample, carefully transfer a drop of each beverage to a different numbered spot on the paper. Be sure that no solid gets transferred in the drop.

Step B Record the number for each sample in your notebook.

Step C Add a few drops of each food coloring to its own microwell, and transfer a drop to the chromatography paper using a new toothpick. Record the number for each food-coloring sample in your lab notebook.

Step D Form a roll with the paper, so that the samples are at the bottom and the spots on the inside.

Step E Carefully staple the roll at the top and bottom, leaving a small gap between the edges of the paper. First make sure the sample spots have dried.

Step F Pour the developing solution into the bottom of the developing chamber so that liquid level is ***below*** the spotted samples. Be sure not to disturb the dye spots.

Step G Cover developing chamber and watch the solvent move up the paper. Be sure to monitor solvent progress, as you will need to remove the paper from the chamber when the solvent has moved to 1–2 cm from the top of the paper.

Step H When solvent reaches this level, remove the paper from the chamber, open the paper roll, and quickly trace the solvent front with a pencil.

Step I Let the paper dry, being sure to notice if the solvent front has moved any farther up the paper. If it has moved as the paper dries, retrace the solvent front. When the paper is dried, circle all colors from the separated dyes with a pencil, and mark the top of each dye with a pencil. Record the relative color shades and intensities of each color in your lab notebook.

Step J Use a ruler to measure the distance between the starting point of the sample and this line at the top of the dye spot, as well as the distance from the starting point to the solvent front.

Calculations

Calculate the R_f value for each dye sample of powdered mix. Compare these R_f values, which are your standards, to those of the unknown dyes in the food-coloring samples.

Post-Lab Questions

1. Construct a data table.

2. Use the R_f values you have calculated, along with your detailed color observations, to try to determine the identities of the dyes in the food-coloring samples.

3. Explain why the colors exhibit different R_f values.

Name _____   Date _____

Instructor _____   Section _____

Experiment

16   Electrolytic Synthesis of Iodoform

PURPOSE

- Perform an electrolysis of potassium iodide with acetone in basic solution to form iodoform
- Analyze and explain the products of oxidation and reduction in the experimental electrolysis

INTRODUCTION

In an **electrolytic cell**, electrical energy is used to cause a chemical change. In a sense, this process is the opposite of that in a **galvanic cell**, where chemical differences cause an electrical current to flow. In electrolytic cells, positively charged cations move toward the negatively charged **cathode**, where extra electrons are pumped to create a surplus. Typically, the positively charged cations are reduced to the metallic atom. Negatively charged anions move toward the positively charged **anode**, where there is a shortage of electrons. The anions are frequently oxidized to their nonmetal atom. These migrations of ions are illustrated in Figure 16.1, a schematic rendering of an electrolytic cell consisting of molten sodium chloride.

Figure 16.1
Electrolytic Cell

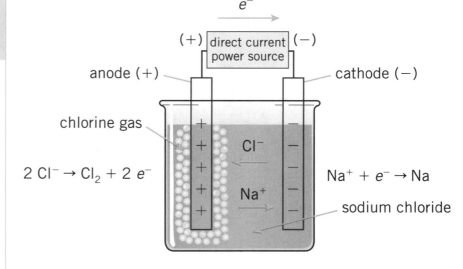

$$2\ Cl^- \rightarrow Cl_2 + 2\ e^-$$

$$Na^+ + e^- \rightarrow Na$$

One of the most important applications of electrolytic cells to the industrial world is the electrolysis of brine, a concentrated solution of sodium chloride, the source of which is seawater. The process thus converts an inexpensive and common raw material into commercially valuable products such as the gases hydrogen and chlorine, as well as sodium hydroxide solution. Chlorine is in turn used in the manufacture of plastics and to chlorinate water for safe drinking. Sodium hydroxide, the most important industrial base, is used in many processes, including the neutralization of acids and the manufacture of paper and soap.

Note that there is the potential for competition for electrons at the electrodes of an aqueous electrolytic cell. At the cathode, the cation of the salt can be reduced. Alternatively, if there is an energy advantage, the water can be reduced to hydrogen gas with formation of base (hydroxides) as a by-product. At the anode, too, there may be competition. Either the anion of the salt can be oxidized, or the water can be oxidized to oxygen gas with formation of acid as a by-product. For the electrolysis of brine, then, the possibilities are as follows.

At cathode:

$$Na^+_{(aq)} + e^- \rightarrow Na_{(s)} \qquad\qquad E^\circ = -2.71 \text{ V}$$

or

$$2\,H_2O_{(l)} + 2\,e^- \rightarrow H_{2(g)} + 2\,OH^-_{(aq)} \qquad E^\circ = -0.83 \text{ V}$$

At anode:

$$2\,Cl^-_{(aq)} \rightarrow Cl_{2(s)} + 2\,e^- \qquad\qquad E^\circ = -1.36 \text{ V}$$

or

$$2\,H_2O_{(l)} \rightarrow O_{2(g)} + 4\,H^+_{(aq)} + 4\,e^- \qquad E^\circ = -1.23 \text{ V}$$

Note that the chloride and the water are oxidized with similar facility, assuming that the chloride concentration is 1 M. To ensure that the chloride is oxidized in the commercial process, rather than the water, the concentration of sodium chloride is kept very high.

The overall desired electrolytic reaction, then, is

$$2\,H_2O_{(l)} + 2\,e^- \rightarrow H_{2(g)} + 2\,OH^-_{(aq)} \qquad E^\circ = -0.83 \text{ V}$$

$$2\,Cl^-_{(aq)} \rightarrow Cl_{2(s)} + 2\,e^- \qquad\qquad E^\circ = -1.36 \text{ V}$$

yielding

$$2\,Cl^-_{(aq)} + 2\,H_2O_{(l)} \rightarrow H_{2(g)} + Cl_{2(s)} + 2\,OH^- \qquad E^\circ = -2.19 \text{ V}$$

Procedure Preview For the preparation of iodoform in this experiment, an electrolysis of aqueous potassium iodide solution is first performed. Freshly prepared iodine, a product of the electrolysis, then reacts with acetone in basic solution to form iodoform, acetate anion, and iodide anion:

$$CH_3COCH_{3(l)} + 3\,I_{2(s)} + 4\,OH^-_{(aq)} \rightarrow CHI_{3(s)} + CH_3COO^-_{(aq)} + 3\,I^-_{(aq)} + 3\,H_2O_{(l)}$$

Pre-Lab
Questions

1. What is a **ketone**? How are ketones named?

_____

_____

_____

_____

_____

_____

_____

_____

_____

_____

_____

_____

_____

_____

_____

_____

_____

_____

2. Determine the formula and draw a molecular sketch of:

   a. acetone

   b. acetate ion

   c. iodoform

Pre-Lab Questions *(continued)*

d. triiodomethane

e. chloroform

f. tribromomethane

3. For the electrolysis of an aqueous solution of KI, write a balanced equation to show the reaction at

a. the anode ______________________________

____

b. the cathode ______________________________

____

MATERIALS

➤ battery
➤ potassium iodide (KI)
➤ two pencil leads

➤ 50-mL beaker
➤ filter paper

➤ acetone (CH_3COCH_3)
➤ 0.1 *M* potassium hydroxide (KOH)
➤ two wires (each with an alligator clip at each end)
➤ #8 rubber stopper
➤ microstir bar (*see Appendix C on page 140*)

PROCEDURE

Step A Obtain a 50-mL beaker and position it on a magnetic stir plate. Add 1.000 g KI and 10 mL distilled water to beaker and mix thoroughly with microstir bar. Add 1.5 mL acetone and mix. Add 0.5 mL KOH and mix.

Step B Place a #8 rubber stopper on the beaker. Obtain two pencil leads, positioning one down each side of the stopper such that the end of the lead is immersed in the solution below. Each pencil lead, an electrode, should touch the solution, but not touch either the other electrode or the microstirbar. Use the alligator clip at one end of each wire to fix the lead electrodes in the desired position.

Step C Attach the opposite end of each wire by its alligator clip to a battery terminal.

Step D Allow electrolysis for at least 10 minutes. Record time elapsed in seconds.

Step E Collect the solid product onto filter paper by gravity filtration. Dry in air overnight.

Step F Find the mass of the product.

Step G Perform a melting point analysis of the solid product.

Calculations

1. Calculate the number of moles of iodoform produced.
2. Calculate the number of moles of electrons required to produce the iodoform.
3. Calculate the number of coulombs required to produce the iodoform.
4. Calculate the number of amperes required of the battery to produce the iodoform.

Post-Lab Questions

1. What is the product of oxidation during the electrolysis? Write and balance an equation to show this. Did you collect this product?

_____

_____

2. What is the product of reduction during the electrolysis? Write and balance an equation to show this. Did you collect this product?

_____

_____

3. Why did you add a small amount of KOH before starting the procedure?

_____

_____

_____

4. How can you be sure that the electrodes were nonreactive—that is, that they did not participate in the reaction?

_____

_____

_____

5. Determine the limiting factor in this experiment. Explain or show calculations to support your contention. Is it possible to calculate the percent yield?

_____

_____

_____

6. Would you expect to attain 100% yield in this experiment? Why or why not?

_____

_____

_____

7. Is iodoform a polar molecule? Draw a **Lewis structure** (apply VSEPRT) to support your contention.

_____

_____

_____

8. Compare the experimental melting point to the theoretical value (found in the *CRC* or other handbook). Calculate percent error.

_____

_____

_____

Name _____   Date _____

Instructor _____   Section _____

Experiment
17   Exploring Electrochemistry

PURPOSE

- Create a galvanic (Danielle) cell and determine the voltage generated by it
- Use the Nernst equation to calculate the concentration of an unknown solution in a galvanic cell
- Create a concentration cell and use the Nernst equation to calculate the concentration of an unknown solution
- Predict an activity series

INTRODUCTION

The branch of chemistry dealing with the exchange of electrons between two species is **electrochemistry**. The electrons move from the species oxidized to the species reduced. There are a number of mnemonic devices to help you to remember the direction of this flow of electrons. One of these is "*LEO* the Lion says *GER*," meaning

Loss of Electrons is Oxidation
and
Gain of Electrons is Reduction

In a galvanic (or voltaic) cell, as you may recall from Experiment 16, chemical differences cause an electric change. Potential differences between substances cause electrons to flow from one species to another, as long as the half-cells are separated by a salt bridge and an external circuit. If the half-cells are in physical contact with each other, the potential difference is wasted as heat rather than as flow of electrons through an external circuit. In contrast to a galvanic cell, an electrolytic cell represents the opposite situation: an externally supplied electric current that forces chemical differences to occur.

The **electromotive force** ("emf") of a galvanic cell may be calculated by combining the values for each half-cell from a table of Standard Reduction Potentials ("SRP") to find E°, the **standard voltage** for the cell. The superscript ("°") indicates standard conditions of one atmosphere, 298 Kelvins, and one molar concentration of all species in solution. If any of these characteristics differs from the standard condition, then the voltage in the cell will be changed. To calculate the altered or nonstandard voltage, you can use the Nernst equation, developed by the Nobel laureate Walther Nernst. In the full form of the Nernst equation, a difference in any of these characteristics can be accommodated:

$$E = E° - \left(\frac{RT}{nF}\right)\ln Q$$

where E = nonstandard voltage; $R = 8.314\,J\,mol^{-1}\,K^{-1}$; T = temperature in Kelvins; n = number of moles of electrons transferred in the redox; F = Faraday's constant (96,500 coulombs mol^{-1}); and Q = trial equilibrium reaction quotient, expressed as $\frac{[products]}{[reactants]}$.

But note: because ions in solution are not affected by pressure over the surface of the solution, and one frequently assumes the standard temperature of 298 K, there is a variant of the Nernst equation used to allow calculation with only a difference in concentrations of ions of the two half-cells. Keep in mind, also, that this form of the Nernst equation uses base-10 log rather than the natural log:

$$E = E° - \left(\frac{0.0591}{n}\right)logQ$$

Because the cell potential depends on the concentration of the ions in the two half-cells, you can construct a galvanic cell with identical half-cells except for the concentrations of the ions. This is called a **concentration cell**. The difference in voltage is apt to be small because all components of the half-cells are identical except for the concentrations. For example, the voltage between a 1.0 M Cu^{2+} solution half-cell and one of 0.010 M Cu^{2+} solution is just less than 0.06 V.

Experimentation with various metals and solutions containing the cations of those metals is fascinating. You can observe the behavior of such situations to establish an **activity series** of the ease of oxidation of certain metals. For example, if you place a piece of solid copper wire into a solution of silver nitrate, you will observe solid silver metal forming onto the copper wire (thus the reduction of Ag^+ to Ag), while the solution in the container becomes blue (thus Cu becomes Cu^{2+}). From this, you can conclude that copper is more easily oxidized than silver. You might verify this conclusion by dropping a piece of silver wire into a solution of Cu^{2+} and noticing that nothing happens, because the more easily oxidized copper is already oxidized.

Procedure Preview In this experiment, you will use the techniques of microchemistry to set up three different electrochemical cells and thus compare the behavior of three different half-cells paired with each other.

1. What is a Danielle cell?

_____

_____

_____

2. In a functioning galvanic cell

   a. at which electrode does oxidation occur? where does reduction occur?

   _____

   b. which electrode gains mass? which electrode loses mass?

   _____

   c. around which electrode does the concentration of cation solution increase?

   _____

   around which electrode does the concentration of cation solution decrease?

   _____

   d. from which electrode and to which electrode do electrons in the external circuit move?

   _____

3. What is the function of a salt bridge?

_____

_____

_____

_____

_____

_____

4. Has all chemistry ceased when the voltage of a galvanic cell becomes zero? Explain.

_____

_____

_____

_____

_____

_____

MATERIALS

- 24-well microplate
- 1 *M* CuSO$_4$
- 1 *M* ZnSO$_4$
- unknown *M* CuSO$_4$ solution
- 1 *M* KCl solution
- sandpaper (or steel wool)

- Cu metal strip
- Zn metal strip
- filter paper
- forceps
- voltmeter

PROCEDURE

I. Initial preparations

Step A Cut a piece of filter paper into a number of strips approximately 0.5 by 4.0 cm.

Step B Place the strips of filter paper into a small beaker containing 1 *M* KCl solution, allowing them to soak up the solution.

Step C Locate two strips of copper metal and one strip of zinc metal, each approximately 0.5 by 4.0 cm.

Step D Use fine sandpaper or steel wool to polish the metal strips. Try to clean off any external corrosion to leave a shiny metal surface. Carefully wipe away any loose particles from the surface of the strips.

Step E Select three clean wells in a 24-well microplate. The wells should be adjacent to each other, in a triangle.

Step F Pour 1 *M* CuSO$_4$ into one well. Pour 1 *M* ZnSO$_4$ into another well. Pour the unknown copper(II) solution into the third well.

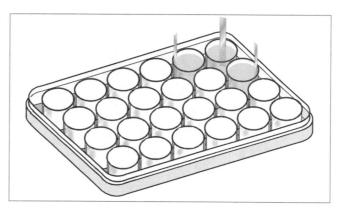

Figure 17.1

Step G Place a strip of Cu metal into each of the two wells containing Cu^{2+} solution and a strip of Zn metal into the well containing the Zn^{2+} solution. Try to stand each strip at the outer edge of its microwell, such that an equilateral triangle is formed with the metal strips at the apexes of the triangle.

II. Creating a Danielle cell

Step A With forceps retrieve one filter paper strip from the beaker of 1 *M* KCl solution. Allow excess solution to drip from the strip back into the beaker.

Step B Using the forceps, carefully drape the paper strip from the well containing 1 *M* CuSO$_4$ solution, across the top of the microwell plate, and down into the well containing 1 *M* ZnSO$_4$ solution. This paper acts as the salt bridge between the two half-cells. Do not allow the paper to contact the metal strips.

PROCEDURE
(continued)

Step C Quickly attach the leads of the voltmeter to the copper strip in one well and to the zinc strip in the adjacent well.

Step D Record the voltage measured by the voltmeter.

Step E Detach the leads from the metal strips.

Step F Use forceps to retrieve the salt bridge paper strip and dispose of it properly.

III. Creating a Concentration Cell

Step A With forceps retrieve one filter paper strip from the beaker of 1 M KCl solution. Allow excess solution to drip from the strip back into the beaker.

Step B Using forceps, carefully drape the paper strip from the well containing 1 M $CuSO_4$ solution, across the top of the microwell plate, and down into the well containing unknown concentration $CuSO_4$ solution. This paper acts as the salt bridge between the two half-cells. Do not allow the paper to contact the metal strips.

Step C Quickly attach the leads of the voltmeter to the copper strip in one well and to the copper strip in the adjacent well.

Step D Record the voltage measured by the voltmeter.

Step E Detach the leads from the metal strips.

Step F Use forceps to retrieve the salt bridge paper strip and dispose of it properly.

IV. Comparing the Zn/Zn^{2+} half-cell with the unknown concentration Cu/Cu^{2+} cell

Step A With forceps retrieve one filter paper strip from the beaker of 1 M KCl solution. Allow excess solution to drip from the strip back into the beaker.

Step B Using forceps, carefully drape the paper strip from the well of unknown M $CuSO_4$ solution, across the top of the microwell plate, and down into the well containing 1 M $ZnSO_4$ solution. This paper acts as the salt bridge between the two half-cells. Do not allow the paper to contact the metal strips.

Step C Quickly attach the leads of the voltmeter to the copper strip in one well and to the zinc strip in the adjacent well.

Step D Record the voltage measured by the voltmeter.

Step E Detach the leads from the metal strips.

Step F Use forceps to retrieve the salt bridge paper strip and dispose of it properly.

Step G Dispose of all solutions as directed by your instructor. Rinse and dry the metals strips, since they are reuseable.

Calculations

1. Use a Table of Standard Reduction Potentials to calculate the cell potential (as voltage) of a Danielle cell.

2. Compare the cell potential that you measured with a voltmeter to that calculated with SRP values. Calculate percent error.

3. Use the voltages that you measured with the concentration cell (Procedure III) and the Danielle cell (Procedure II) to calculate the molarity of Cu^{2+} ion in the unknown.

4. Use the voltage that you measured with the cell in Procedure IV and that of the Danielle cell to calculate the molarity of Cu^{2+} ion in the unknown solution.

1. Write a balanced chemical equation to show the reaction that occurs in a Danielle cell.

_____

_____

_____

2. Write the line notation shorthand for the Danielle cell.

_____

_____

_____

3. Did the voltage that you measured with a voltmeter match the cell potential that you calculated from SRP values? Explain why the two might not have matched.

_____

_____

_____

_____

_____

_____

4. For each of questions 4a through 4e, explain your reasoning. Predict the effect on the cell potential of the Danielle cell if you

   a. increased the molarity of the Cu^{2+} ion

_____

_____

_____

_____

_____

_____

_____

_____

_____

_____

_____

_____

_____

Post-Lab Questions *(continued)*

b. increased the molarity of the Zn^{2+} ion

c. poured K_2CO_3 solution into the $CuSO_4$ solution

d. increased the size of the metal strips

e. increased the temperature to 35°C

Post-Lab Questions *(continued)*

5. Did you find the same concentration for the unknown Cu^{2+} solution in Calculation 3 and Calculation 4? Would you expect to find the same value? Explain.

_____

_____

_____

_____

_____

_____

_____

_____

_____

_____

_____

_____

_____

_____

6. Based on your observations and calculations in this experiment, which is the more active metal, copper or zinc? Explain your reasoning.

_____

_____

_____

_____

_____

_____

_____

_____

_____

_____

_____

_____

_____

Name _____   Date _____

Instructor _____   Section _____

Experiment

18 Determining the Solubility Product Constant of Calcium Hydroxide

PURPOSE

- Determine the solubility product constant (K_{sp}) of $Ca(OH)_2$ by various methods, including measuring the dry mass and recording the pH of a saturated solution
- Determine the solubility product constant of $Ca(OH)_2$ by titrating a saturated solution with HCl, finding the equivalence point of titration, and calculating molar solubility
- Compare the three laboratory methods for precision and analyze possible sources of error

INTRODUCTION

The **solubility** of a compound in water may be considered the maximum amount of solute that dissolves in a given amount of water at specified temperature and pressure. When the maximum amount of solute has dissolved, the resulting solution is called a **saturated solution**. If more solute is added, it will not dissolve but rather remain solid. At this point, an equilibrium between the aqueous and solid solute, called **solubility equilibrium**, may be achieved.

Figure 18.1

Because of a dynamic equilibrium between the solid and its ions, any addition of solute to this saturated solution will only contribute to the amount of solid.

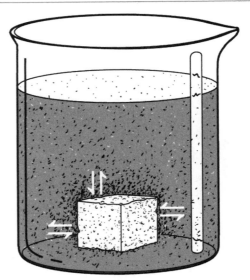

Although a solute may be a molecular compound, most solubility equilibria investigated in chemistry involve ionic compounds. In investigating the solubility of ionic compounds, it is helpful to adopt a change in mindset that is opposite to the way we study solubility in precipitation reactions, where the solid is a *product*, as in this example:

$$2 \, Ag^+_{(aq)} + CrO_4^{2-}_{(aq)} \rightarrow Ag_2CrO_{4(s)} \qquad (1)$$

By contrast, solubility equilibrium reactions for ionic compounds are written for the *solid reactant* that is dissolving in water and dissociating into ions. The solubility for the silver chromate precipitate formed in reaction (1) would be written as

$$Ag_2CrO_{4(s)} \rightleftharpoons 2 \, Ag^+_{(aq)} + CrO_4^{2-}_{(aq)} \qquad (2)$$

The equilibrium constant for solubility equilibria is called the **solubility product constant**, or K_{sp}. The K_{sp} expression for reaction (2) is $K_{sp} = [Ag^+]^2 [CrO_4^{2-}]$. The solid is not included in such an expression, because its ionic concentrations do not change, no matter how much solid is present.

Investigating reaction (2) further, one can find that $K_{sp} = 1.2 \times 10^{-12}$ at 25°C. However, note well: this value does not help you determine the concentration of silver chromate that actually dissolved in the solution to make it saturated; for this one must calculate the molar solubility of silver chromate. A saturated solution must be made before a precipitate forms. In "equilibrium speak," the reaction quotient, Q, must be greater than K_{sp} to have a precipitate form. Working backwards, it is relatively straightforward to calculate the molar solubility and the concentration of all ions at 25°C, in the following manner:

Let $x = [CrO_4^{2-}]_{Eq}$. Then

	$Ag_2CrO_{4(s)} \rightleftharpoons$	$2 \, Ag^+_{(aq)} +$	$CrO_4^{2-}_{(aq)}$
Initial (M)	----------	0	0
Change {Δ} (M)	----------	$+2x$	$+x$
Equilibrium (M)	----------	$2x$	x

Because $K_{sp} = [2x]^2 [x] = 1.2 \times 10^{-12}$
$$4x^3 = 1.2 \times 10^{-12}$$
and $x = 6.7 \times 10^{-5} \, M = [CrO_4^{2-}]_{Eq}$

By substituting this value of x into the table above, we then find that

$$[Ag^+] = 2x = 1.3 \times 10^{-4} \, M$$

The value of x also represents the molar solubility of silver chromate. Solubility is sometimes represented as mass of solute/volume of solution. Conversions between this form of solubility and molar solubility require molar mass conversions and volume conversions. For example, the solubility of silver chromate in g solute/1.00 L solution is

$$\frac{6.7 \times 10^{-5} \text{ moles Ag}_2\text{CrO}_4}{1.00 \text{ L}} \times \frac{331.74 \text{ g Ag}_2\text{CrO}_4}{1 \text{ mole Ag}_2\text{CrO}_4} = \frac{2.22 \times 10^{-2} \text{ g Ag}_2\text{CrO}_4}{1.00 \text{ L}}$$

In order to measure a solubility product equilibrium constant, one must have a saturated solution. Then, by determining the concentration of one ion in the saturated solution and using stoichiometry, the K_{sp} can be calculated.

Procedure Preview The solubility product constant, K_{sp}, for calcium hydroxide will be determined by different methods and the results compared to find the best method for determining this K_{sp}. In the first method, a known volume of a saturated solution of $Ca(OH)_2$ is put in a dried beaker, the mass of which has been measured, and the water driven off in an oven. The mass of the solid $Ca(OH)_2$ is then measured to determine K_{sp}. The second method employs a calibrated pH probe to measure the pH of the saturated solution of $Ca(OH)_2$. The $[OH^-]$ is determined and used to calculate K_{sp}. In a third approach, the saturated $Ca(OH)_2$ solution is titrated with HCl. The resulting titration curve is used to determine the equivalence point of the titration, and then K_{sp} is determined using the molar solubility of $Ca(OH)_2$. As a variation on Method 3, your instructor may direct you to follow Method 4, a microscale titration of saturated $Ca(OH)_2$ solution using various indicators.

Pre-Lab Questions

1. Taking the K_{sp} for $Ca(OH)_2$ from your textbook, calculate

   a. its molar solubility

   b. its solubility in g/100 mL

2. Calculate the theoretical volume of 0.020 M HCl that must be added to 25.00 mL of saturated calcium hydroxide, in order to reach the equivalence point of the titration.

3. Predict the pH at the equivalence point of the titration of $Ca(OH)_2$ with HCl, explaining your reasoning thoroughly.

   _____

   _____

   _____

   _____

   _____

Method 1: Drying

MATERIALS

- tongs
- pipet bulb
- balance
- saturated solution of $Ca(OH)_2$
- 50-mL beaker
- 25-mL volumetric pipet (or other volume-measuring device)
- drying oven (*alternatives:* hot plate; or Bunsen burner with ring, ring stand, and wire square)

PROCEDURE

Step A Use tongs to manipulate the beaker throughout this procedure.

Step B Place the 50-mL beaker in drying oven, allowing it to dry completely.

Step C Measure the mass of the beaker.

Step D Using a volumetric pipet, add 25.00 mL of saturated calcium hydroxide solution to the beaker and place in drying oven.

Step E Let beaker with $Ca(OH)_2$ solution dry completely, then remove from oven. Let cool.

Step F Measure mass of beaker and solid calcium hydroxide.

Step G Return beaker to oven, allowing to dry longer. Mass again after cooling to ensure that all water evaporated. If mass decreases, repeat drying until there is no major mass change.

Method 2: Initial pH

Note: This section may be skipped if you are conducting Method 3, because the initial pH determined in Step G of Method 3 provides the data needed to make the calculation of K_{sp}.

MATERIALS

- pH meter
- saturated $Ca(OH)_2$ solution
- 50-mL beaker
- pH standards (pH=4.00 and pH=10.00)
- distilled water (in squirt bottle)
- magnetic stirrer
- microstir bar

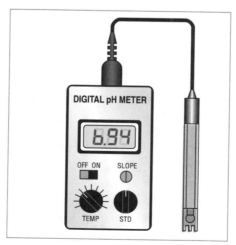

Figure 18.2 First, you will need to calibrate your electronic device for measuring pH.

PROCEDURE

Step A Calibrate the pH meter according to your instructor's directions.

Step B Rinse pH meter tip with distilled water and pat dry with paper towel.

Step C Pour some saturated $Ca(OH)_2$ into the beaker, adding enough to cover bulb of pH meter.

Step D Allow pH reading to stabilize while solution is being stirred (either manually or using the stir bar and magnetic stirrer). Record the pH of this solution.

Method 3: Titration Curve

MATERIALS

➤ pH meter
➤ saturated $Ca(OH)_2$ solution
➤ 0.020 *M* HCl solution (standardized)
➤ 100-mL beaker
➤ 50-mL buret
➤ buret clamp
➤ clamp
➤ ring stand
➤ microstir bar
➤ magnetic stirrer
➤ volumetric pipet (25-mL or a combination of others)
➤ pipet bulb
➤ pH standards (pH=4.00 and pH=10.00)
➤ distilled water (in squirt bottle)

PROCEDURE

Step A Calibrate the pH meter. Your instructor will give you specific instructions to do so.

Step B Rinse the pH meter tip with distilled water and pat dry with paper towel.

Step C Prepare buret by rinsing it with 0.020 *M* HCl and removing any air bubbles from tip.

Step D Fill buret to 0.00-mL mark.

Step E Measure 25.00 mL of saturated $Ca(OH)_2$ solution, using a volumetric pipet, and place in 100-mL beaker along with a micro stirbar.

Step F Place pH meter in solution, waiting for pH reading to be constant.

Step G Record pH when 0.00 mL HCl is added. *(This is the pH to use to calculate K_{sp} for Method 2.)*

Step H Add 1–2 mL of HCl. Allow the solutions to mix thoroughly for 1 minute.

Step I Record the pH when the reading has stabilized, and enter the exact volume of acid added (to 0.01 mL).

Step J Repeat Steps H and I. *Be sure to record <u>total</u> volume of acid added, not the amount of HCl added after last recorded volume.*

Step K Keep repeating until 50.00 mL of acid has been added. Be sure to add *smaller incremental volumes of HCl* as you approach the volume of acid needed to reach the equivalence point (per calculation from Pre-Lab Question 2), **or** as the pH begins to change rapidly after HCl is added. Continue to add smaller volumes until change in pH decreases per volume of HCl added.

Method 4: Microscale Titration

MATERIALS

➤ saturated $Ca(OH)_2$ solution
➤ 0.020 M HCl solution (standardized)
➤ 24-well microplate
➤ microstir bars (3)
➤ magnetic stirrer
➤ 1.0-mL volumetric pipet
➤ micropipet
➤ bromophenol blue
➤ phenolphthalein
➤ bromocresol green

PROCEDURE

Step A Measure 0.80 mL of saturated $Ca(OH)_2$ solution into each of 3 micro-wells and place a microstir bar in each well.

Step B Add 1 drop of each indicator in a separate well of saturated $Ca(OH)_2$ solution.

Step C Place a sheet of white paper on the stir plate, then place the microwell plate on the magnetic stirrer with the appropriate well on the center of the stir plate. Turn on the stir plate. Prepare buret by rinsing it with 0.020 M HCl, removing any air bubbles from tip.

Step D Fill buret to the 0.000-mL mark.

Step E Titrate until appropriate color change is permanent. You must be patient close to endpoint, because it takes a few seconds for complete mixing of solution and color change of the indicator.

Step F Recenter the plate on the next well containing saturated $Ca(OH)_2$, and titrate this sample.

Step G Repeat Step F for third and final sample.

Calculations

In your lab report, include your computations and conclusions for the following questions.

1. Write a balanced chemical equation that describes the solubility of calcium hydroxide and write the K_{sp} expression for it.
2. Find the theoretical K_{sp} value, citing your source.
3. Calculate the K_{sp} of calcium hydroxide for *each* of the lab methods followed. Show **all** work in each case.

   Method 1: Find the molar solubility of $Ca(OH)_2$ and use this to calculate K_{sp}.
   Method 2: Use the $[OH^-]$ from the initial pH (before HCl is added) to calculate K_{sp}.
   Method 3: Graph the titration curve of pH versus volume (mL) of 0.020 M HCl added. On the titration curve, determine volume (to appropriate significant figures) of HCl added to reach the endpoint at pH = 7.00. With this volume, determine the concentration of $Ca(OH)_2$ in the saturated solution, and then calculate K_{sp}.
   Method 4: Use stoichiometry to calculate molarity of $Ca(OH)_2$ and then K_{sp}.

Post-Lab Questions

1. What K_{sp} do you get from Method 1?

_____

_____

_____

2. What K_{sp} do you get from Method 2?

_____

_____

_____

_____

3. Using the initial pH reading from Step G of Method 3, calculate the K_{sp} of $Ca(OH)_2$.

_____

_____

_____

_____

4. Is the experimentally determined pH at the equivalence point of the titration in Method 3 consistent with the theoretical value? If not, cite one possible error source that would lead to your actual experimental value. Explain thoroughly.

_____

_____

_____

_____

5. Which method is the most accurate? Explain your answer completely, giving examples of possible error sources in each case.

_____

_____

_____

_____

6. When a saturated solution of $Ca(OH)_2$ is stored, why is it best to be sure that some solid is present?

_____

_____

_____

_____

7. What would happen to the calculated value for the K_{sp} of $Ca(OH)_2$ if there were an air bubble in the buret tip when you started the titration, and this air bubble were drained during the titration? Explain your reasoning in detail.

_____

_____

_____

_____

8 a. Suppose that the saturated solution of $Ca(OH)_2$ were stored in an open container at constant temperature and half of the water evaporated. What would happen to the calculated K_{sp} value? Explain.

_____

_____

_____

_____

b. What changes would you observe in the storage bottle after the water evaporated?

_____

_____

_____

_____

9. Many orange juices that are fortified with calcium contain a mixture of calcium hydroxide/citric acid/maleic acid. How does mixing the calcium hydroxide with these acids increase the molar solubility of $Ca(OH)_2$? Explain in detail, including balanced chemical reaction equations to support your explanation.

_____

_____

_____

_____

10. Compare your results for the microscale titration for each indicator. Should all of these indicators result in the same K_{sp} value? Why or why not? Be sure to include a theoretical titration curve as part of your answer.

_____

_____

_____

_____

Appendix

"Care and Feeding" of the Buret

The **buret** is defined as "a graduated glass tube used to deliver variable volumes of liquid, usually equipped with a stopcock to control the liquid flow" (*McGraw-Hill Dictionary of Chemical Terms*, 1984). Marked to 0.1 mL increments, it can and should be read to 0.01 mL. As such, it is a precision device and should be treated with care and respect.

Preparation of Buret for Use

Clean the buret with a very dilute detergent solution (one drop of detergent per liter of water) and a buret brush (a very long test tube brush). Rinse several times with tap water. Then rinse with at least five 10-mL aliquots of dH_2O (distilled water), for which a wash bottle is very convenient. Be sure that some water runs through the stopcock and tip, and that water runs freely from the buret without any drops adhering to the sides. Also, check that the buret does not leak and that the stopcock turns freely.

Before using the buret in an experiment, rinse it once with a 10-mL aliquot of the experimental solution that is to be delivered. Only then fill it with the appropriate amount of solution.

In case of clogging: If the tip of the buret clogs, try soaking it overnight in weak acid. If this does not clear the tip, insert a very fine wire—gently—to try removing any blockage. If you still make no progress, put the buret aside and consult with an experienced colleague.

Cleaning Buret after Use

If appropriate, rinse the buret once with the opposing solution (as, for example, in an acid-base titration). Do not rinse with any solution that will cause a precipitate to form within the buret; it is, after all, a measuring device and not a reaction vessel. Follow up by cleaning with dilute detergent solution and a buret brush, rinse with tap water, and then rinse at least five times with dH_2O.

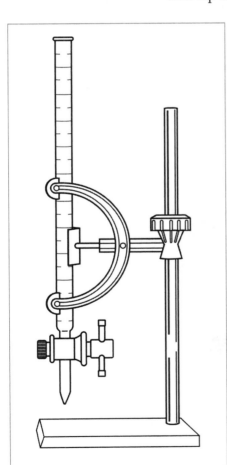

Figure A A 50-mL buret with buret clamp and stand.

Storage of Buret

Clean the buret stand carefully so that it is bright white for the next user. Use a very mild abrasive if necessary. Place several mL dH_2O in the buret to keep the stopcock wet. Adjust the buret in the stand so that it almost touches the surface of the base of the buret stand. Place the buret back in the chemistry storage area.

B How to Make Microburets

Microburets are useful for transferring small volumes of solution, as required in Procedures for Experiment 8 (Finding Mass Percent of Acetic Acid in Vinegar), Experiment 9 (Analysis by Redox Titration), and Experiment 18 (Determining the Solubility Product Constant of Calcium Hydroxide).

MATERIALS

➤ ~7-cm length of amber latex tubing (with 3/8-in. inner diameter, 1/8-in. thick wall)

➤ 5-mL luer lock syringe

➤ paper clip

➤ 2-mL pipet graduated to 0.01 mL (*Note:* the authors have successfully used serological pipets for this purpose.)

PROCEDURE

Step A Roll each end of the latex tubing back on itself about 1 cm.

Step B Stick the luer lock end of syringe into one end of the tubing and unroll tubing back over end of syringe. You may cut the luer lock covering off, but the authors find that the covering keeps the tightest seal between the tubing and syringe.

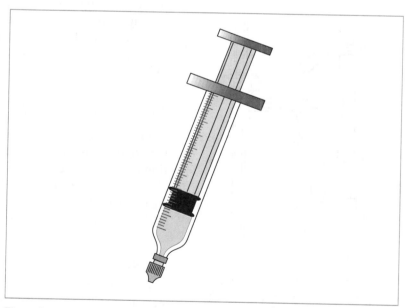

Figure B Use latex tubing to connect the luer lock end of the syringe to a pipet graduated to 0.01 mL.

PROCEDURE
(continued)

Step C Using a paper clip, remove cotton batting from end of pipet.

Step D Stick this end of pipet into the other rolled end of the tubing; unroll tubing over end of pipet.*

Step E Your microburet is now complete. It is best to pull the plunger on the syringe out a little before submerging the tip in solution, because sometimes this additional air is needed to force out the remaining solution after the completion of experimental measurement/titration.

Step F Practice drawing and releasing water to get the feel for adding 1 drop at a time and for reading the buret to 0.001 mL. As with any buret, it is appropriate to rinse it at least twice with the solution you are about to use before filling it for use in the experiment.

Step G Some people hold microburets in their hands vertically, whereas others may find them easier to handle when they are placed and held in buret clamps.

*At this point, it is possible to affix a 100-μL pipet tip (yellow) onto the other end of the pipet to minimize drop size. The authors have found that such tips can shoot off or leak, even if glued on. Therefore, they are not recommended for use on our microburets. Experimental results have not suffered due to larger drop size.

Appendix

How to Make Microstir Bars

Microstir bars may be required in procedures where microwell plates are used (as in Experiments 8, 9, 10, 13, 16, and 18).

MATERIALS

➤ capillary/melting point tubes
➤ metal paper clips
➤ wire cutters
➤ triangular file
➤ Bunsen burner
➤ lighter
➤ crucible tongs

PROCEDURE

Directions are given here for using tubes with either one or both ends open. Whichever procedure you follow, it is most efficient to cut the appropriate number of paper clip lengths and pieces of glass tube all at once, then seal each microstir bar, one by one.

I. For tubes with one end closed

Step A Unbend paper clip and use wire cutters to cut into appropriately sized pieces. Cut only from straight sections of paper clip so they will slide completely into tube.

Step B Determine appropriate length of tube needed to hold each paper clip length. Score one side of tube a few millimeters past this length using the sharp edge of a triangular file.

Step C Locate the scored section of tube and turn this side away from you.

Step D Hold tube so that both thumbs are behind the score and the tube is held securely, using your index fingers as well. Carefully apply pressure to tube, using your index fingers to pull it toward you. Carefully increase pressure until the tube snaps at score. (***Caution:*** Do not cut your finger on a sharp edge of broken glass.)

Step E Take closed end and turn it down, holding the tube upright. Slide cut piece of paper clip inside tube, letting it fall to closed end.

Step F Turn on gas and carefully light Bunsen burner.

Step G Using crucible tongs, hold tube at closed end so as not to let piece of paper clip drop out. Now place open end at the hottest part of the flame, the tip of the inner cone.

Step H Seal the open end of the tube, rotating it gently to help ensure even heating and melting of glass. (Enjoy the nice yellow-orange color emitted from excited sodium atoms in the glass!)

PROCEDURE
(continued)

Step I When end is sealed, place microstir bar on lab bench to cool. *Caution:* hot and cold glass look the same. Do not burn yourself by grabbing a hot stir bar. Let it cool completely before handling, or use tongs to manipulate until cool.

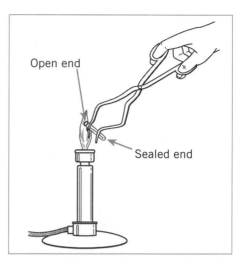

Open end

Sealed end

Figure C

II. Using tubes with both ends open

Step A Unbend paper clip and cut into appropriately sized pieces using wire cutters. Use only straight sections of paper clip so they slide completely into tube.

Step B Determine appropriate length of tube needed to hold each length of paper clip and score one side of tube about 5 millimeters past this length, using edge of triangular file.

Step C Locate the scored section and turn this side away from you.

Step D Hold tube so that both thumbs are behind the score and the tube is held securely with your index fingers as well. Carefully apply pressure to the tube using your index fingers to pull the tube ends toward you. Carefully increase pressure until the tube snaps at score. (*Caution:* do not cut a finger on a sharp edge of broken glass.)

Step E Turn on gas and carefully light Bunsen burner.

Step F Using crucible tongs to hold tube, place an open end at tip of inner cone of flame—the hottest part of the flame.

Step G Seal the open end of the tube, rotating it gently to help ensure even heating and melting of glass. (Enjoy the nice yellow-orange color emitted from excited sodium atoms in the glass!)

Step H Take sealed end and turn it to the bottom, thereby holding the tube upright. Slide cut piece of paper clip inside tube, letting it fall to sealed end.

Step I Use crucible tongs to hold filled tube at sealed end so as not to let paper clip piece drop out. Place unsealed end at tip of inner cone of flame, the hottest part of the flame.

Step J Carefully seal this open end of the tube. (*Caution:* remember that hot and cold glass look the same. Be sure not to burn yourself by grabbing a hot stirbar. Let it cool completely before handling, or use tongs to manipulate until cool.

How to Construct a Pycnometer

According to one source (the *American Heritage Dictionary of the English Language*), the *pycnometer* is a standard vessel used in measuring the density or specific gravity of materials. The word comes from the Greek words *pyknos*, meaning "dense," and *meter*, meaning "a device to measure." Pure substances may be characterized and identified by their physical properties, including density, whether in the solid, liquid, or gaseous phase. A device such as a pycnometer can be used to measure these mass-volume relationships.

In constructing the pycnometer, its inside volume is established with great precision. The flask is filled completely to that volume with a liquid and then the entire device plus its contents are massed. With the mass of the liquid corresponding to that volume determined precisely, one calculates the mass-volume ratio, or density, of the unknown substance. Pycnometers are used extensively in the chemical and related industries, typically measuring volumes in the range of liters. Here is the chance for you to construct a pycnometer on a small scale, appropriate for measuring samples of a milliliter or so, as required in Experiment 6, Analysis of a Volatile Liquid.

MATERIALS

- ➤ glass tubing
- ➤ triangular file
- ➤ Bunsen burner
- ➤ forceps (or crucible tong)
- ➤ Pasteur pipet

PROCEDURE

Step A Measure a distance 2 cm to 4 cm from the end of a length of glass tubing.

Step B Use a triangular file to make a notch in the tubing at that measured length. Do not saw the file across the tubing. Instead make a single long, firm stroke. A proper stroke will coax a characteristic high-pitched song from the glass.

Step C Lay the tubing flat on the table, turning the notch away from you. Place the tips of your thumbs together behind the notch with the flats of your thumbnails touching each other. Spread your fingers as far as possible along the length of the tubing, as if you are placing them on a piano keyboard. Applying pressure at the tips of your pinkies, turn your hands slowly and gently away from each other until the glass snaps.

Step D Because the inclination of most people is to apply too much force at first try, you may need to pick up the shattered remnants of the tube from the floor and place in the designated container for broken glass. Repeat Step C, but this time use much less force. Just think *"Break!"* to the glass tube as you slowly rotate your hands. Be aware that the edges of the newly broken ends are very sharp.

Step E Light a Bunsen burner. Hold the glass tubing piece at its middle with a forceps or crucible tong and use the flame of the burner to seal one end. Hold the tubing vertically, keeping the end to be sealed at the hottest part of the flame, the tip of the inner blue cone. (Use of a higher temperature flame—a Meeker burner, for example—will speed this process.)

Step F Repeat the process at the other end of the glass tubing, but do NOT seal the tube entirely. Leave an opening of 3–4 mm.

Step G Allow your pycnometer to cool. Test the size of the opening that you have left by trying to insert the tip of a Pasteur pipet, which should *just* fit into the cavity of the pycnometer.

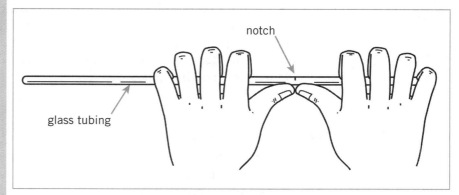

notch

glass tubing

Figure D Turn hands slowly and gently apart, applying pressure at the little fingers and holding thumbs steady.

ALTERNATE PROCEDURE

Step A Measure a distance 3–4 cm from the open end of a Pasteur pipet.

Step B Use a Bunsen burner flame to soften the glass at the designated point. Be sure to rotate the tube so that the heat is distributed all the way around the circumference of the pipet.

Step C As you feel the glass soften, draw the tube apart. This will leave a long tail on the piece of glass.

Step D Hold the piece of glass vertically with forceps or a crucible tong. Place the tail end of the piece briefly into the flame to ensure that it is sealed and to round off any extended, comet-like tail.

Step E Turn the piece to the other open end and hold it in the flame until it is almost sealed. Leave an opening of 3–4 mm.

Step F Allow your pycnometer to cool. Test the size of the opening that you have left by attempting to insert the tip of a Pasteur pipet, which should *just* fit into the cavity of the pycnometer.

How to Construct an Apparatus for Gas Kinetics

Reactions that produce gas are common, but it can be difficult to measure the quantities of gas that are produced over time. One way to approach this problem is to realize that the pressure exerted by the gas will increase as the quantity of gas generated increases. An apparatus that gives a visual sign whenever a threshold pressure is exceeded is a perfect solution. Such a device can be easily constructed for use in the laboratory, as required in Experiment 13, Kinetics: Differential and Integrated Rate Laws.

MATERIALS

➤ Beral-type pipet
➤ one-hole rubber stopper (#2 size)
➤ micropipet tip
➤ 50-mL Erlenmeyer flask

PROCEDURE

Step A Cut the top of the bulb off a plastic Beral-type pipet, creating a flat top, open to the atmosphere. At the other end, cut the stem to leave a 25-mm stub.

Step B Insert the stem end of the pipet into the *top* opening of a #2 one-hole rubber stopper, leaving the open end of the pipet bulb extending from the top of the rubber stopper.

Step C Obtain a white or yellow plastic micropipet tip (spares are likely to be available from your Advanced Placement Biology or molecular biology program). Insert this tip into the *lower* opening of the one-hole stopper. Push the micropipet tip into the stopper until it is flush with the lower end of the stopper. The tapered end of the micropipet tip should now extend into the bulb portion of the Beral-type pipet.

Step D Insert the rubber stopper into the mouth of a 50-mL Erlenmeyer flask.

Using the Gas Kinetics Apparatus

To use this device, place any reactants into the Erlenmeyer flask. Immediately insert the kinetics apparatus into the mouth of the Erlenmeyer flask and fill the bulb of the Beral-type plastic pipet with water. Although distilled water is not required, it is convenient to use distilled water from a plastic wash bottle. Any gas generated by the reaction in the Erlenmeyer flask will build up until there is sufficient pressure to cause the gas to escape from the micropipet tip. The gas formation may be easily noted, and tallied, as a tiny bubble issuing forth from the micropipet tip into the water reservoir within the open bulb of the plastic pipet.

The AP Chemistry Exam
Preparation and Helpful Hints

PART I: MULTIPLE CHOICE (90 minutes, 45% of your total score)

There are seventy-five questions with several choices each. Often some questions are presented in groups and formatted in these ways:

➤ five answer choices followed by a series of questions; *or*

➤ three answer choices in Roman-numeral form followed by a series of answers with different combinations of choices I, II, and III.

The rest of the multiple-choice questions are in standard question-and-answer format. Simple math may be required, but no calculators are allowed in Part I. You can do scratch work in the booklet, though the problems can usually be figured by estimation. You will be provided with a Periodic Table. No equation sheet is provided. You must use a #2 pencil to shade in the bubbles on the answer sheet.

$$\text{Raw score} = \text{number correct} - (0.25 \times \text{number wrong})$$

Helpful Hints for Part I

If a question is completely unfamiliar, do not answer it because there is a penalty for guessing. However, if two or more of the options can be eliminated, use your best judgment in choosing one of the remaining options.

Because you will be pressed for time on the multiple-choice section, you must use your time efficiently. Use the triage method: answer the easy questions immediately. Do not spend too much time on any one problem because there will be some easier ones near the end of the test. Mark problems you recognize as "do-able but time consuming" with a ✓ and, if you have time, come back to them later. If you know a problem involves a topic you have not studied—or do not remember—mark it with an **X** and do not return to it.

PART II: FREE RESPONSE (90 minutes, 55% of your total score)

Calculators are permitted for the first forty minutes (Part A: Questions 1–3). Then time will be called and your calculators must be put away for the remaining fifty minutes (Part B: questions 4–9). A Periodic Table, table of standard reduction potentials, and a table of equations and constants will be provided.

Part A: (forty minutes; calculators allowed; periodic table, standard reduction potentials, equations always provided; sometimes other charts)

Question 1 is *always* a required equilibrium problem (K_p/K_c, K_a, K_b, K_w, K_{sp}; acid-base neutralization; common ion effect; le Chatelier's principle; buffers). Remember that a later part of a question can frequently be answered without the preceding parts, and it is frequently easy. Question 1 represents 20% of your free-response grade.

Of questions 2 and 3, you choose only one. These two problems will be quantitative. Some possibilities include:

➤ thermodynamics (enthalpy, entropy, free energy)

➤ electrochemistry (emf, Nernst equation, and K and G)

➤ kinetics (rate law, rate constant)

➤ solutions (concentrations, colligative properties)

➤ elemental analysis (empirical formulas, molar mass).

The one question you choose will represent 20% of your free response grade. In the near future, this choice between quantitative questions may be replaced by a single required quantitative question.

Part B: (50 minutes; *no calculators;* Periodic Table/other tables are available)

Net Ionic Equations Question 4 is a required problem where you will write net ionic equations to show the formulas of reactants and products of chemical reactions. There will be eight reactions listed and you must answer five. Each reaction is worth 3 points (1 point for reactants and 2 points for products).

Your final answers should be in the form of net ionic equations. They do not need to be balanced, nor do you need to write state symbols. Keep in mind that reactions in aqueous solution frequently have water as a product. Also remember that you have access to a Periodic Table and a set of equations in the form of a Standard Reduction Potential table. Question 4 represents 15% of your free response grade.

Essays Questions 5 and 6 are both required essays. One of these essays will be related to the laboratory, so look over the suggested topics in this Lab Manual and review your lab notebook. Questions 7 and 8 are both essays. You must choose only one of them. In the near future, this choice between qualitative essays may be replaced by a single required qualitative essay.

Topics for the essays can come from anywhere in the AP Chemistry curriculum. Atomic structure and bonding is a very common topic. Each of the three essay questions represents 15% of your free-response grade.

Helpful Hints for Part II

If a question seems unfamiliar, try to link it to one of the main topics covered in class or think of any formulas or theories related to the topic that might help answer the question. Remember that you have access to a Periodic Table and a set of equations.

When you are given an option of which questions to answer, select carefully before starting to respond. There are no points for style, so do not intentionally pick a more difficult problem, thinking that it will make you look better.

Very little is subtracted for math errors, so set up each problem clearly and show all work to get the maximum amount of partial credit. Label all quantities. Pay attention to significant figures (you are allowed ± 1), especially for pH figures where the significant figures are only to the right of the decimal point. When in doubt, report your answer to 3 "siggie figgies." If you do not have time to work through the math, at least put down the units. Be sure to *box* your answers on the quantitative problem.

In Part A of Part II, if you need an answer from a previous part to answer a later part, but could not answer the earlier part, just make up an answer to the earlier one; for example:

$$\text{"Let K = 345 for part A ..."}$$

and solve the later section accordingly.

You may return to Part A while you are working on Part B, but you will not have access to your calculator.

You do not need to erase spectator ions in your net ionic equations for question 4; rather, simply cross them out.

When you answer an essay question, be sure to make a clear statement that addresses the question—an *assertion*. Then support your assertion, or contention, with chemical knowledge—the *justification*. Restating the question is a waste of your time and merely annoys the Reader grading your paper. Remember that you have about 90 seconds of the Reader's time to convince him or her that you know what you are talking about. Do not shovel great gobs of redundant or superfluous verbiage that lengthen your response but add nothing significant to its quality. Avoid all statements that equivocate, such as

"ΔG may or may not be positive, negative, or zero in this situation depending on whether or not this temperature is warm or cold and the concentrations of the solutions are dilute or concentrated."

Make strong, definitive statements and support them to the best of your knowledge.

MATERIALS FOR THE EXAM

Bring the following to the Exam:

➤ sharpened #2 pencils

➤ an eraser

➤ pens (blue or black)

➤ a scientific calculator with fresh batteries

➤ a watch

➤ a can of soda and some high energy snack food. Chocolate is especially good. (The authors personally recommend M&Ms while you are writing and a Mounds bar or two for the break.)

One final hint: GET PLENTY OF SLEEP THE NIGHT BEFORE THE EXAM!